THE WILD ANALYST

The Wild Analyst

The Life and Work of Georg Groddeck

by Carl M. Grossman, M.D. and Sylva Grossman

George Braziller, New York

ACKNOWLEDGMENTS

In the course of preparing the text, the authors used many references, and wish to thank the writers and publishers of such material for permission to quote. Specifically, we owe our gratitude to:

Erik Erikson and the W.W. Norton Co., for *Childhood and Society*, New York, 1950.

Michael Balint, for *Final Contributions to Psychoanalytic Technique*, by Sandor Ferenczi, New York, Basic Books, 1955.

Sigmund Freud Copyrights, Ltd., for the Freud letters.

Vision Press, for Georg Groddeck's *The Unknown Self, Exploring the Unconscious*, and *The Book of the It*.

Butterworth & Co., London, for Dr. William Inman's "Emotion and Eye Symptoms," in *Modern Trends in Psychosomatic Medicine*

Basic Books, for *Life and Work of Sigmund Freud*, by Ernest Jones, New York, 1955.

Journal of the American Psychoanalytic Association, for Leo Rangell's article, "The Nature of Conversion," Vol. 7, No. 4, October, 1959.

Farrar, Straus & Co., for Theodor Reik's *Listening With the Third Ear*, New York, 1949.

Many people lent encouragement and assistance in this project, the most important being the late Dr. Frieda Fromm-Reichmann, without whom there would have been no book. Others, who deserve more than passing mention, are Marga-

5

rete Honegger, Oscar Köllerström, William Inman, Hanna Gindes, Kate Pastron, and the dozens of people who sent us their recollections and good wishes.

In Memoriam
To Dr. Frieda Fromm-Reichmann

"*I think we shall gain a great deal by following the suggestion . . . of Georg Groddeck, who is never tired of pointing out that the conduct through life of what we call our ego is essentially passive, and that, as he expresses it, we are 'lived' by unknown and uncontrollable forces . . .*"

—Sigmund Freud

CONTENTS

"I am a wild analyst."

Thus did Georg Groddeck introduce himself in 1920 to the Psychoanalytic Congress at The Hague. And then he proceeded to speak, in an informal, unorganized, discursive demonstration of the process of free association. He made a few friends that day, and several enemies.

The father of psychosomatic medicine, Groddeck would have been dubious about the term. *Psyche* and *soma* were not for him separate entities but facets of one whole. His patients, most of them, presented somatic complaints. His therapy was what he called "psychic treatment." On the other hand, when Dr. Felix Deutsch referred a patient with a severe compulsive neurosis, he treated the man with violent massage and scalding hot hydrotherapy.

"Such strange ways of treatment Groddeck used," said Deutsch with admiration, "knowing very well the psychological reasons for their effect."

In this generation, a handful of internists, a score of psychiatrists are familiar with the pioneering work of Georg Groddeck. A few poets discovered him early, and recognized his genius, as Thomas Mann saw greatness in Freud—Auden, Spender, and Lawrence Durrell among others.

To some of the older psychoanalysts today the very mention of his name is embarrassing. Some were his pupils, among them a prominent teacher of analysis who said in a recent letter, "My own professional development and that of the field has gone in an entirely different direction . . . I would not wish my name to be associated in any way with that of Dr. Groddeck."

The anxiety in the lines is understandable. The good doctor regards his "Groddeck period" as indiscreet, youthful, and outgrown. Speculation, experiment, and daring flights of imagination were permissible in the '20's, but now we must have respectability, caution, and agenda.

There is, however, another group, scattered all over the world. Grateful and loquacious, Groddeck's former patients have never forgotten him. From Israel, one woman spoke for them:

"Everything I ever heard from Dr. Groddeck impressed me deeply and has remained with me and become part of my being. He did not cure your illness, he healed you."

His contemporaries reacted with strong feelings, some with veneration, some with dislike, even disgust. He encouraged his patients, his pupils, and friends to allow themselves knowledge of their hidden, forbidden wishes. An easy thing to say, almost a cliché, but a difficult thing to accomplish. Those who succeeded saw him as a saint and a liberator. Others felt threatened, frightened, angry. A personal meeting or even a first reading of his books often called up violent feelings. The reactions were almost always emotional, and had little to do with any intelligent evaluation of what he was saying. It did not matter what the background of the listener or reader happened to be; feelings were high wherever his influence was felt.

Georg Groddeck has been dead for more than thirty years. Among his admirers the legend is already obscuring the reality. There is a persistent story that he was a "healer" without formal training of any kind; he is said to have been a writer who turned to medicine in his middle years; he is supposed to have been a defecting disciple of Freud, and he is also said to have been the real brain behind Freud. He is called a wild man, an angel, a lunatic, and a genius.

One point is indisputable. Nobody who knew him in life was indifferent to him. Nor can anyone be who encounters his work today.

THE WILD ANALYST

1

"GOOD PEOPLE, BAD PEOPLE, AND GRODDECKS"

He conformed to no pattern. When he applied for membership in a psychoanalytical society, he wrote diffidently to Freud, "Perhaps I don't quite fit in." He was right, although he tried to behave well and added, only half-humorously, "I am easy to get along with."

From the day of his birth, the world was not ready for him. When he was born, on October 13, 1866, several days ahead of schedule, the wet nurse was elsewhere engaged, and there was no milk. Caroline Groddeck had nursed only her first-born, Karl, and Georg was the fifth. There were three boys and a fragile little girl of fifteen months ahead of him.

The new arrival was ugly, with ludicrously large ears. There was not even a family name left for him. It was decided that he should be named for George Marchand, his father's friend, and he was immediately tagged with Marchand's nickname, Pat.

His first few days were spent squalling in hunger. Twice a day a wet nurse hurried in and offered her breast for a few minutes. The infant screamed, but there was no help for it.

"To have to go hungry is not a kind welcome for a newborn infant," Georg Groddeck said of his first days, but he thought that by comparison with other hungry babies he had come off well.

Then Bertha arrived, plump and loving. Bertha stayed three years, so though the child made a poor beginning, he soon thrived, and early became adept at handling his environment.

He was the youngest, but he had not the unique position of the family baby. That position belonged to his sister, Lina. By the time he was two years old, Pat was almost as big as Lina, and physically stronger. He could best her in games, but he was not permitted to slap her or tease her or provoke her to tears. The reason, given to him many times with an air of self-evident logic, was simple: Lina was ill. Thus, very young he realized the astounding power of illness. Lina needed neither strength nor wit. She received whatever she desired by the simple expedient of being ill. Wonderful! He resolved to try it when he had a chance.

Caroline Groddeck took her two youngest children with her one evening to a meeting. The children were put to bed in a room adjoining that of the grown-ups. "I don't know how the notion came into my head that the greater the number of witnesses the more impressive would an illness be," Groddeck later recalled, "but anyhow, I suddenly had the idea of setting up a coughing duet with my sister, in the hope of ensuring a day's holiday from school for both of us." The results were gratifying. The meeting adjourned early, and brother and sister remained at home the following day.

The lesson was learned for all time: weakness was strength. Illness was a powerful weapon.

He was not nearly so successful in efforts to have his way with his brothers. Instead, as the youngest, he bore the brunt of their jokes. He was their favorite object of ridicule, the baby who mispronounced words, who misquoted, misunderstood, and made all sorts of comical mistakes. His idiocies were detailed at mealtime, his stupidities recalled, his ignorance hooted at. There was, of course, a defense against all of it. He became cautious and silent. He spoke freely only when alone with Lina. He shared a bedroom with her, and could be depended upon to be considerate. Even in criticizing his sister, he was gentle. He watched uneasily one day as she piled cover after cover on her doll, tried to stop her, and finally burst out, "All right, but you'll see she'll be smothered!"

It was that overheard exclamation, as he watched the little scene, that decided Dr. Karl Groddeck. A three-year-old, showing a grasp of cause and effect! The boy should become a doctor. Medicine was not to be for young Karl, the eldest, though he was intelligent. He had inherited his mother's love for literature, he must do something with words; besides, there was something physically wrong with him, perhaps a mild epilepsy, with fainting fits. Nor could the father imagine the second-born, Hans, as a doctor. As for Wolf—no. But Pat must become a doctor, there was no question about it. And when the father asked his son if he thought he would like to become a doctor, the boy recognized the question as a compliment and assented eagerly. It was settled.

His mother was neither pleased nor disappointed. To her, the practice of medicine was slightly better than a trade, involving perhaps a little more skill than cabinetmaking. Literature was worthwhile. Her father had been a scholar, the first historian of German literature, and his name, August Koberstein, was known to every person of culture. Koberstein's library was the most valuable possession of the boys' school at Pforte, which he had honored by his presence as a teacher for more than fifty years. He had been personally acquainted with all the famous poets of his time and had been the acknowledged leader of the literary society called, after the twelfth-century poet, the Vogelweide. To Caroline, this was worthwhile.

She often spoke to her children of her father, who was dead before Pat could know him. A learned man, she said, a

true adventurer of the mind. His library, acquired over a lifetime, contained some of the rarest books in existence. One
book of Koberstein's was so valuable that a man had committed murder to obtain it, and had been caught and hanged. Pat
was disappointed to learn that Grandfather Koberstein acquired the book without shedding blood, merely by bidding
for it at auction.

Koberstein had been dead for years, twice the length of
Pat's life, and still Caroline wore black. Karl Groddeck hated
black. For Caroline's birthday, father and sons conspired to
end the wearing of mourning forever. Karl bought a dress,
reddish-brown, neither somber nor gay, and gave the boys
money to buy silk for trimming the dress. All was wrapped
and presented to Caroline as a gift. She never wore the dress.
She continued to wear black for the rest of her life.

Even then, as a child, Pat was aware of an unbridgeable distance between his parents. Caroline saw nothing praiseworthy
in Karl's success as a physician. His ability to get along well
with all sorts of people, his gift for friendship, his easy manner, all signified a sort of commonness to her. He was too
good-tempered, he demanded too little of people, he was not
sufficiently discriminating. His one laudable accomplishment,
in his wife's view, was his graduation thesis. Entitled *de
morbo democratico—nova insaniae forma*, it was said to have
influenced Nietzsche.

In 1930, Georg Groddeck answered a letter questioning
him about his father and Nietzsche. To Professor Vaihinger
he wrote:

> From 1856-1883 my father had a healing spa in Kösen.
> In the '70's his home was the intellectual center of
> many from far and near. Among other groups, the
> German literary society (the so-called Vogelweide)
> met there under the leadership of Koberstein, my ma-

ternal grandfather. The well-known Etruscan authority, Korssen, who saw much of Nietzsche in Naumberg, was a daily guest in the home of my parents. I consider it likely that Nietzsche knew my father or that at least he often heard mentioned the title of the dissertation to which we are referring, and if he did personally meet my father, he must have kept a strong impression. My father had something to give to everyone he met. Nietzsche must also have met my mother in 1859-1860, since at that time she lived a whole year in Pforte. My mother was the typical daughter of an impressive man, and mistress of all knowledge of the time.

Caroline and Karl had met when he was a student at Pforte. When Karl fell ill, of some sort of heart disease, he was nursed for several months in the Koberstein home. During that illness the young people became engaged. It was Caroline's mother who cared for the patient, and the young man became devoted to the older woman. The daughter never spoke of her mother with the admiration she held for her father. Her mother was a perfectly ordinary woman with something of Karl's facility for gathering people to her. A dubious distinction this seemed to Caroline, if not a fault. But however Frau Koberstein appeared to her daughter, she was a memorable person to others. She had been dead fifty years when Elisabeth Forster-Nietzsche and Gersdorff, Nietzsche's friend, spent a whole evening talking about her.

Karl tried to behave as though medicine meant only a livelihood to him. He made a literary center of his home in Bad Kösen, where he had moved his practice to be near Caroline's parents; he gave up his old friends, even Lessing, the grand-nephew of the playwright—in short, he tried in every way to please his wife.

"I believe he honestly tried to become a Koberstein," his son wrote later. "He sought the company of his wife's parents and tried to adopt their outlook on life, but it could not be done. He was too lonely, too strong . . ." To his youngest son, Karl was the strongest, wisest man in the world. He was a stern father, though he was also affectionate, and his children adored him. But he never found a role in which his wife accepted him. He was not quite fine enough for her, though his family was well-placed and high-born. His father had been mayor of the free city of Danzig, and later a Speaker in Parliament. Indeed, the Groddecks, who had their own pride, considered that Karl had married beneath him.

Years later, Georg Groddeck wrote, "To the Groddecks there were three kinds of people—good people, bad people, and Groddecks." He reflected that they had little reason to feel superior except that they were not stupid.

To the son, the father's personality was unforgettable. "My father had something to give to everyone he met," he wrote to Vaihinger. But not to Caroline. And the son said regretfully of his father's efforts to become a Koberstein, "As I look back I realize that it was the source of all the friction which threatened their married life."

The two disagreed about nearly everything. Karl withheld criticism for long periods and then burst out in sudden anger. When Caroline let her son's hair grow long, dressed him in starched frocks, and sent him to school to a *Madchenschule* with his sister, he was silent. Until one day, when it was as if he had suddenly looked at the boy and realized what was going on. The hair was cut short, the frocks exchanged for boys' clothing, the girls' school discontinued.

2

SCHOOL DAYS

Georg Groddeck was nine when he was enrolled in Dr. Raabe's school for boys. For the first time, he was away from his sister. It was strange to him, but it was an emancipation. His brothers were all at Pforte. He was no longer anybody's fool. He began to learn. For three years he was at the top of his class at Dr. Raabe's school. Then came the news that he was to be sent to boarding school.

Pforte was not far away, only half an hour's journey from Kösen. He knew something about it already: Grandfather Koberstein's books were in the library, there were holidays at Easter and at Christmas, the food was bad, punishment was severe. He had always known that some day he would be sent to Pforte, yet the talk of his departure took him by surprise. He believed he was reluctant to leave his mother. She was sometimes cruel, especially to his father, but she could also be kind and loving, as when she had taken Georg into her bath with her.

When he looked back, as an adult, Groddeck said, "I was a 'mother's boy,' a petted nestling, and the separation from my mother when I went to school brought real suffering." There is no question about his suffering, but he was not "a petted nestling." His mother demonstrated, time after time, that if she had a favorite at all, it was Karl, her first-born. Bummi, as he was called, was studying philology.

By the time Pforte became an inevitability for the near future, Georg had forgotten the episode of coughing to control the grown-ups; he had forgotten, at least for a time, his early lesson in the power of weakness. Nevertheless he fell ill. It was a "real" illness—that is, there were symptoms and signs as well as subjective complaints. The cause was undetermined and the diagnosis indefinite, but the doctors termed it "nerve fever" and treated it with bed rest, purges, and a light diet. For weeks he lay in bed with high temperatures, headache, and an overpowering sleepiness. At the same time his face was so discolored and scabbed with impetigo that his mother could scarcely bear to look at him.

Despite all his sufferings, he left for Pforte on schedule, still weak and subject to fatigue, but quite well enough to leave home.

Pforte proved all he had feared. The school had been built in the twelfth century as a monastery. Surrounded by high stone walls, it was a fortress and a prison. Except for two hours on Sundays, the gates were kept locked, and even on Sundays nobody was allowed outside the walls who had not passed a full week without reprimand.

Young Groddeck was a sinner from the beginning. He could not seem to avoid doing what was forbidden. His feeling of being imprisoned was scarcely endurable. He was among the younger students; he was peculiar looking, with intense eyes and over-sized ears; and he was, on top of everything else, a chronic bedwetter. At first, he broke rules in defiance, with the result that he lost Sunday privileges at once. Later he committed other crimes—he played cards, made tea, climbed over the walls, and smoked. He was thrashed. When the effort was not deemed sufficient, he was locked into a tiny cell. He spent so many hours in this isolation that he earned the title of "jail king." After being an excellent student for years, he became a mediocre one, berated for laziness, for being ill-prepared, for yawning and dozing in class. His masters had him examined by the school doctor to see if there might be a physical basis for his indolence and drowsiness. The doctor found nothing wrong, but thwarted the disciplinarians by suggesting that the boy seemed to need more rest than most people.

The sentence at Pforte—six years—was relieved by holidays and the long summer vacations. At home, the boy was neither lazy nor sleepy. He was seldom alone, never sought solitude, accepted everything without question, and rarely took notice of anything unpleasant. School holidays were interludes of bliss in an otherwise almost unrelieved dreariness. He felt that he learned absolutely nothing at school; "At Pforte none of the teachers knew how to get hold of me . . ." He had only one friend, a quiet boy who was kind to him and with whom he drank beer on rare occasions away from school.

In his fourteenth summer, his sister Lina was confirmed in the Protestant Church. Lina, in what may have been a hope of pleasing her mother, underwent a spell of religious fervor during the preparation for confirmation. Every morning while the mother brushed and braided her daughter's hair, the girl read aloud from the Bible. Caroline found the whole attitude boring and silly.

On the day of confirmation, just after Lina had left for church, Caroline told the others that they were not to attend. She gave no explanation, and her youngest was too well-trained to question her. He spent the morning sitting at the edge of a ditch, poking at leaves and twigs with a cane his father had made him from the branch of an olive tree. The older boys had such canes, too, but his was the smallest. He was suddenly dissatisfied with its smallness. When he reached home, he realized he had lost his cane, and though he returned to the ditch and retraced his steps, it was never found. He went back to school without it.

The return of that autumn was particularly difficult, for

no reason he could understand. The sojourn at home had not been as blissful as usual. His mother's behavior with Lina was disturbing, and his father seemed to have grown more remote. At school, things were no worse than usual. He was confined, scolded, thrashed, and lonely, but at last the bedwetting was ended.

A year later, in 1881, he found everything at home much changed, but in his joy at being free, he hardly cared. He heard serious talk between his parents, and he knew of the events, but none of it had anything to do with him.

His father had invested heavily in a building venture with two men, one of them a friend, the same George Marchand for whom Georg was named. The other man was a retired colonel about whom Karl knew little. Marchand was knowledgeable in the business of contracting and had proved capable and energetic when he suddenly fell ill. Within a few hours he was dead. He had not altered his will for years, so there was no provision for continuing the building, and his heirs wanted nothing to do with it. Then the colonel disappeared, and with him all the money Karl had invested with Marchand.

At once it seemed that crowds of people were owed money by the trio, and now all demands were made on Karl. Landowners, working men, opportunists—everyone wanted something. Karl was named in more than twenty separate lawsuits.

Caroline was dutiful, if unsympathetic. She discharged her servants and silently suffered the humiliation of doing her own housework. The end of months of litigation found Karl temporarily freed of obligation, but his practice had been neglected and he had been harried mercilessly. "Worse still," his son wrote, "my parents were utterly ruined: everything belonging to them, including the house in which we had all been born and brought up, had to come under the hammer, and our proud position was lost forever."

The last hope, that Karl's father would leave them something, was shattered when the old man died and left everything to his second wife. Even then, there was a remote chance that the widow might help the Groddecks; unfortunately the lady lost her entire inheritance in an ill-advised speculation. The house gone and the practice gone, the family moved to Berlin, where Karl had been promised a job as a panel doctor.

Through the months of trouble, Georg Groddeck was hardly perturbed. He had complete faith that his father would somehow manage. He felt confident that in no time at all, Karl would have a loyal following in Berlin, even a patient he would call *Cauchemar* (nightmare), like the woman at Kösen who was always sending sweets to the children. Indeed he looked forward to the change of residence as a rather exciting way to spend the school holidays.

In retrospect, he had further thoughts about those years. He spoke about a photograph in which his own likeness was a good one, in contrast to most others, and observed:

> According to my own judgment and the judgment of people who are fond of me, few pictures exist which show the true expression of my nature. One is a picture of brothers and sister. It represents me as a boy of ten, standing upright, with the head bent a little forward. The sad dreamy look goes off to the distance. The picture was taken as a surprise for my mother's birthday (July 12, 1877). At this time we either knew or had a presentiment that our family house would be lost . . . the dreamy-sad expression I consider true, in contrast to other such photographs . . . In the years between 10 and 16 I was always greeted by my relatives with the exclamation: "Just look, the dreamer is coming!" I have only a few memories of this period of repression which ended in a serious scarlet fever.

At sixteen, the summer holiday was spent in sickbed. The scarlet fever promised to prevent his returning to school. He was in bed for weeks, mainly because of a complicating kidney disease, but he recovered in time to go back to school. He was warned against strenuous physical activity. The order was no hardship; Georg was becoming more and more thoughtful and solitary.

3

FATHER AND SON

The last holiday, at Christmas in 1884, was memorable. With the explanation, somewhat offhand, that it might be "just as well" for him "to get used to interviewing the sick," Karl took the boy with him on house calls. On the way, they had talks about medicine, about life, the boy's future.

Dr. Groddeck had no respect for medical traditions. He was a heretic in medicine, "went his own way, right or wrong, and showed no respect for science either in word or in deed." He thought there was too much hocus-pocus in medicine, too much observance of established techniques, too little questioning. Only one living physician earned his praise, Ernst Schweninger, Bismarck's doctor. Schweninger, arrogantly contemptuous of the opinions of his colleagues, made his own decisions and adapted every treatment to suit the needs of the patient.

Karl was disturbed about a tendency he saw in his son. When the boy admitted that he had quarrelled with the only friend he had made at school, his father spoke sternly: "Hang onto this friendship," he said. "You children are all in danger of having a trait of your Mamma's. She attracts people, and, in fact, especially worthy people, but it is her misfortune that she cannot stand it. She feels that she loses herself in her friends and so she pushes them away. They become a danger to her very being. Think of that. Hang onto what you have."

The boy nodded silently. He knew this trait in his mother. She pushed away not only friends but her husband and children. Affection made demands on her which she was unwilling to meet. His father was enriched by love; his mother tried to protect herself from it. His father's patients, even the chronic complainers who had come year after year to the spa, were volubly grateful for his attentions, and he received more from them than his fees and the tokens of embroidered sofa pillows.

Although Dr. Groddeck wanted his son to learn to talk to patients, he was not allowed to enter a patient's house. Karl gave different excuses—the danger of contagion, the patient's morbid shyness, the presence of a disagreeable relative. Even as a child, Georg had known there was something special in the way his father handled patients. Perhaps a visit at home made for an intimacy that was not to be watched by an outsider. Sometimes Karl came out looking exhausted.

Georg knew how difficult things were for his father in Berlin. His job as a panel doctor brought barely enough money for the necessities. There were still debts remaining from the housing affair, and even lawsuits. For three years, the boy's confirmation had been postponed because there was no money to buy the required black suit. He was past seventeen before he was confirmed. The whole ceremony seemed meaningless to him, save the motto he was given: "I thank you, God, that you were wroth with me," which he felt had some significance not yet clear.

The final year at Pforte was the best. Seniors were allowed outside the walls twice a week. They usually spent their precious free hours in a beer garden. One day, only a month before the final examinations, they drank more than usual, or perhaps they were euphoric with the prospect of their approaching freedom. At any rate, they began to sing loudly.

None of them noticed a passerby who stood glowering with disapproval. Pforte had a reputation for being one of the finest schools in Germany, and one of the strictest. The boys were reported to the school authorities. The next day, Georg was called before a solemn meeting of the full faculty. He was given a harsh lecture, ordered to remain in his room, and told that only respect for his family prevented his immediate expulsion.

He was in despair. An official letter was sent off to his parents in Berlin, but before Karl could reply, a master interceded unexpectedly, declaring that young Groddeck had a good mind and had been guilty of mere youthful exuberance. He was allowed to take his examinations, passed easily, and had reached Berlin before his father could reply to the threat of expulsion.

When he came home after matriculation, in the spring of 1885, Georg noticed with shock that his father looked old and ill. Karl confided in no one and allowed no expression of solicitude. He said that he was quite well; not even his wife knew that he was suffering from a recurrence of the symptoms that had first made him ill during his schooldays at Pforte. The return of the symptoms now, he realized, was ominous.

Dr. Groddeck sought to keep his youngest son near him. Arrangements had been made for Georg to begin in September as a free student at the university. In the months that intervened Karl encouraged him to study and took him into the consultation room; he wanted him to learn how to write case histories and prescriptions. Georg enjoyed watching his father at work. At that time, much of his practice in the office consisted in examining healthy men who had to be certified before registering for health insurance. Karl talked easily with these men, and had no trouble setting them to talking about themselves. They addressed him with respect but without constraint. The young man thought his father's simple, dignified manner excellent in a physician.

One morning Georg had left the consultation room for a few minutes and was going back when he heard a patient calling to him to say that the doctor had fainted. By the time he reached his father, Karl was somewhat recovered and was sitting up in a chair. His right arm hung limp, but he made little of it. He said he had felt ill for a moment, he was better now, and would have a glass of water. "You need say nothing about this to Mamma," he said.

Karl resumed his examinations of patients and saw every one who came that day. To his son, it was miraculous; it could only be due to his father's indomitable will. But late that afternoon there was another collapse. Karl was carried unconscious to bed. When he opened his eyes he could only mumble unintelligibly. His entire right side was paralyzed. After some days, he improved slightly, but his speech was thick and difficult to understand; he used incorrect words, his vision was patchy. Then the paralysis seemed suddenly gone, and he would not permit them to call a doctor to see to him. But gradually his mental condition deteriorated so markedly that a physician had to be called in. Georg noticed that whenever the doctor entered his room, his father seemed to improve. His speech became clearer, his breathing eased, his mind was more alert. The change persisted as long as the doctor remained.

It became increasingly difficult to care for the patient at home. He could not breathe unless he sat upright. They put him into a chair, but he was so weak that the slightest movement made his head fall forward, and he could not lift it, but had to sit with his chin on his chest, until someone lifted his head for him. To the son it was heart-breaking; such feebleness in a man like a giant oak, a man like a force of nature. He wrote:

. . . we came to the idea of standing behind his chair and supporting his head, and my eldest brother and I took it in turns to do this in shifts of two or three hours, my mother also sometimes taking a turn. As I stood for hours behind him, I was struck by his peculiar way of breathing—characteristic of heart-patients. First he took a long deep breath, then gradually lightened his breathing until it almost disappeared; then came a dreadful pause when life itself seemed to stop, but at last he revived and the whole rhythm started afresh. Whoever has been with such a sufferer will realize the terror of this experience for a boy who knew nothing of the world or of God. Through some strange chance I discovered that if, when first the breathing showed signs of disturbance, I bored with my thumb into the space between the two muscles at the back of the neck so as to press down upon the vertebra, the breathing would become normal again. In this way I have kept the symptom at bay for hours at a time. I was over-joyed about this and was still too inexperienced to guess that my observation was at fault and my success illusory, so I got the idea firmly fixed in my mind that I would be a sort of wonder-doctor. To this idea, this unlimited faith in my healing powers, I ascribe much of my success. . . .

He was wrong about the treatment, but the experience made it clear to Georg Groddeck for all time that he was destined to be a doctor. Perhaps he never had a doubt. Nowhere in his writings or in recorded conversation did he voice the slightest uneasiness about his father's choice of profession for him.

Yet, in choosing to become a physician he knew he displeased his mother. Indeed, her attitude was made clear during her husband's illness. Faced with the knowledge that Karl was not going to recover, she decided that Georg must become the chief breadwinner for the family. She made arrangements to send him to Russia as a tutor, where his food and lodging would be provided and he could send home the greater part of his earnings.

Karl still lay propped high on pillows in the Catholic hospital where he was finally accepted as a charity patient through the intervention of a Dr. Vollmer. For days he lingered, fighting for every breath, until on the last night there was a distinct change in his face and they all realized he was dying. Georg was told to go to sleep; his mother would sit by the bedside and watch. When he awoke in the morning he was told his father had been dead for hours.

He could not believe it. He was taken to see the body, but the waxen face he looked at was not his father's face. One of his brothers began to weep heart-rendingly, Caroline's eyes were red, but Georg's feeling was anger. His father had stolen away.

The anger persisted through the funeral. He watched his brothers and sister and thought he knew what they felt, but he had no such feelings himself. This was the first death in his experience, and his future reaction to death was always to be the same—anger. He did not respond to death with grief, though he felt grief in other circumstances. He could experience a sense of loss, a chance remark could cause him pain, but death roused anger. "The death of relatives and friends has never made me sad," he said. "I felt that with their dying they had wronged me."

Karl's death left Georg with a terrible sense of having been abandoned by his father. Soon afterward, his mother concluded arrangements to send him away. Help came suddenly and miraculously. Young Karl, now nearly thirty, was offered an excellent position as an editor on the *Vossischen Zeitung*. The salary was generous, enough to care for all of them, enough for Georg to go on to the university.

No one in the family questioned the coincidence of such a fine position materializing exactly when their need was the greatest. It was not until many years later they learned what had happened. Dr. Groddeck's old school friend, Lessing, though long alienated, had heard of the family's difficulties and had created a position for his friend's son. In his gratitude, Georg for once confused cause with effect. "I have to thank him for so much," he said, "it would be impossible to talk of it." He spoke, not of Lessing, to whom he truly owed much, but of his eldest brother.

In the autumn, a month before his nineteenth birthday, he entered the Kaiser Wilhelm University in Berlin and began his medical studies. He was still resentful, still lost, a child forsaken by his father. But within a year he was working hard, learning, fully alive for the first time since he left home for Pforte. He had found a new father in one of his teachers, Karl's idol, the greatest physician of them all—Ernst Schweninger.

4

SCHWENINGER

Like Karl Groddeck, Ernst Schweninger was loudly amused by the nonsense that went under the name of science, but unlike Karl he had not distinguished himself at a university, or written an important treatise; he had done nothing except cure sick people. Probably self-taught in great part, Schweninger was unique.

He took an immediate fancy to young Groddeck. He taught him to doubt every claim he could not personally prove, to question every cure he could not duplicate, to regard the physician as a mere catalyst, setting curative processes in motion. He also taught him to regard as harmful every drug or device that did not demonstrably do good.

Forthright, vulgar, blunt, profane, Schweninger often ordered bizarre treatment, and his handling of Otto von Bismarck was typical.

At sixty-eight, Bismarck had been forced to retire to his country estate "to re-establish his health." His diet, despite chronic indigestion and a dozen related symptoms, was hardly that of an invalid. Emil Ludwig, in his biography *Bismarck*, describes a meal at which the ailing chancellor ate "freely" of soup, eels, cold meat, prawns, lobster, smoked meat, raw ham, roast meat, and pudding. (One of the chancellor's complaints was loss of appetite!) Schweninger was called in for consultation, and he agreed with the other physicians that unless something was done at once Bismarck would not live six months; he was irritable and apathetic, suffering from headaches, varicose veins, insomnia, colic, swelling of the legs, and pain in the face. Schweninger agreed to undertake the care of the patient, but not in consultation with other physicians; he would be accountable to nobody but Bismarck himself.

Ludwig describes the procedure:

> He makes the chancellor get up at eight in the morning to do exercises with dumb-bells; the whole day the patient is to eat nothing but herrings. When Bismarck exclaims, "You must be absolutely mad!" Schweninger rejoins: "All right, Your Highness, you had better call in a veterinary!" Thereupon Schweninger takes his leave. This high-handed proceeding establishes his power over Bismarck, who submits. For a fortnight now, the new doctor does not leave his patient's house. Food and drink, getting up and going to bed, work and sleep, are meticulously supervised. At the end of this period there has been marked improvement. Schweninger leaves the house for the first time. Instantly the patient orders a "triple portion of buttermilk." He has violent gastralgia, followed by jaundice, and departs for Friedrichsruh. There the doctor once more keeps close watch on him, and subsequently in Kissingen and Gastein does not leave him to himself for a single day. After a couple of months, the patient is practically well, and admits that he can return rejuvenated to the treadmill. By dominating instead of allowing himself to be dominated, Schweninger saves Bismarck's life.*

---

* An addition to Ludwig's story is told by Dr. Martin Grotjahn, whose father, Alfred, was a student of Schweninger's. When Bismarck became restive under Schweninger's regime, the doctor allowed him two days a week in which to indulge himself as he chose. When this did not satisfy Bismarck, Schweninger took away one of the days of indulgence.

Schweninger rarely used drugs, but often employed strange diets. He advocated exercise, hydrotherapy, and massage. He did not underestimate the fourth tool he employed, absolute control, and employed it consciously. Excellent physicians had failed with Bismarck because they allowed themselves to be intimidated by the patient. Schweninger was intimidated by no one. But autocrats are not made in medical schools; he had difficulty teaching his method. He held frequent seminars with his students and gave special attention to those he considered promising. They discussed cases and forms of treatment, but again and again it became obvious that a physician could not merely put on the façade of authority; he had to have authority in him.

At some time during their course of study, Groddeck and Alfred Grotjahn were picked out by Schweninger as showing real promise. The great man began to spend extra time with them. He hoped that they would become his assistants and eventually take over his practice.

Besides being an inspiring teacher, the doctor was truly gifted in the art of massage. His enormous hands were powerful and at the same time marvelously delicate; with one hand he could span his entire broad chest. His fingertips knew all the body's muscles, tendons, nerves. Such knowledge could be taught, and Schweninger trained his chosen two to a high degree. As they neared the end of their university training, he decided that they should be present at all consultations. Groddeck found the opportunity exciting and fruitful, but young Grotjahn was frequently offended by Schweninger's manners and language.

One day a new patient presented herself, a middle-aged countess, highly cultivated and genteel. The complaint, ubiquitous in the nineteenth century as in the twentieth, was chronic constipation. Schweninger spent a minimum of time on the physical examination. He even interrupted the patient's

description of previous experiences with physicians and reme-
dies and began to berate the woman.

"I have heard enough," he said. "I understand perfectly.
For years you have abused your gut with gluttony. You have
abused your bowel with purges. Now you come to me because
after all these years your asshole is rebelling. The treatment is
simple. I am told you have a beautiful garden. Use it. Go out
into the garden every morning and squat."

The countess was pale with shock. "In the *garden?*" she
whispered.

"In the garden. And do not come back to me until you
can truthfully say, 'Doctor, this week I have made a nice turd
every day in the garden.' "

The patient departed. A few minutes later, Grotjahn also
took his leave. It was too much. He could hardly have
brought himself to talk to anyone, and certainly not to a
countess, so crudely. He was sure there must be some other
way to practice medicine, and he went off to find it. Groddeck
stayed on with Schweninger, always at his heels, imitating his
bearing, his scowl, his assurance, his delicate or powerful massage, his colorful vocabulary. There was a man!

In 1889 he graduated, and like his father he wrote a
thesis, but his thesis influenced nobody. A drug then widely
used in the treatment of skin diseases was hydroxylamine. He
investigated the drug thoroughly. He wrote that his research
proved the drug was of no value; it was superfluous, "and
whatever is superfluous in medicine is harmful." Hydroxylamine continued to enjoy undiminished popularity, and
finds its way into ointments to this day.

Groddeck now had Schweninger's invitation to become
his associate. But first, as the payment for his free education,
he owed eight years of service to the army.

He rarely spoke afterward of this period except to remark that he found military life harsh and distasteful. He did
not become resigned to the army; it was Pforte over again—

restrictions, regulations, and stupidities. At the university he had seen his family regularly, but as an army doctor, a long way from home, this was impossible. In the middle of his term of service he received a long, complaining letter from his mother. Had he so completely forgotten her that he could not write to her now and then? She had not had a word from him for six months.

The letter was put aside. He intended to answer it when he had a free hour. A few days later he was summoned to her bedside. He arrived on September 20, 1892, to find that he was too late; she was unconscious and died without waking. Just like his father, she had stolen away in his absence. He felt wronged; he also had a feeling of guilt. "Everyone belonging to our civilized society whose mother has died," he wrote later, "believes that he is guilty of her death, believes it even when the mother has died away from him."

Until this time there is no record of Groddeck's having any serious interest in women. He was no longer a stern-faced boy with large ears. He was tall and broad-shouldered, with piercing blue eyes. Although in every photograph he has a fierce, staring look, this may be explained by his attitude toward picture taking. "Get on with it, then," were his words, and he would remain rigid until the ordeal was over. Those who knew him say that his photographs give no indication of his real appearance. Women found him attractive, and he was certainly not unaware of their existence.

> I loved them very constantly, and very unconstantly, for I remember that for hours at a time I would stroll about the streets of Berlin for the sake of seeing some bit of femininity whom I had met by chance and never come to know, but who occupied my fantasies for days and weeks. The list of such dream loves is unending, and up to a few years ago was added to nearly every

day. My actual erotic experiences had nothing in the world to do with these loves of my soul.

Two years after his mother's death, he met Else, his first serious love. Else was a married woman.

When I look back over my emotional life I realize that, in every case where my heart was engaged, I broke in as a third upon a friendship already existing between two persons, that I always separated the one who roused my emotion from the other, and that my affection cooled as soon as I had succeeded in doing so.

Else was no longer interested in her husband, an army officer; her two small children were frightened of their father, and the young man's infatuation gave her a way out. Her husband was willing to allow a divorce, and by the time Groddeck was released from the army and had gone to Schweninger's sanitarium in Baden-Baden, she had won her freedom and joined him.

The new family, which included Groddeck's sister Lina, settled in Baden-Baden where the chief attraction of Schweninger's sanitarium, the celebrated obesity cure, was to be administered by Groddeck. In itself the cure was not unusual —it involved vigorous massage, hydrotherapy, and a strict diet, but Schweninger's fame was so widespread that many visitors came to observe. One of the visiting doctors, an ophthalmologist named Hermann Cohn, wrote a paper on the cure. Professor Cohn was the father of Emil Ludwig, and, like his son, was much impressed with Schweninger's methods.

Groddeck's success in Schweninger's sanitarium led him to risk opening a sanitarium of his own. In 1900 Lina borrowed a small sum of money and made a down payment on a wooden house on Werderstrasse in Baden-Baden. The family moved in; the place was painted and refurnished, and the third floor was fitted with special tubs for mineral baths. Groddeck thought the building attractive; to him its defects were charming. The main entrance was separated from the road by a ditch, a waterless moat, and a wooden bridge was necessary, a touch that delighted Groddeck. There was even a tower, completely useless, and described by a contemptuous patient as "irrelevant."

The house was pleasantly situated on a hill high above the main street of the city and many of the rooms had wooden balconies that allowed a view of the Black Forest.From the balconies could be heard the gurgle of a stream running far below. Groddeck found everything about his house wonderfully suggestive of Kösen, with the difference that this was his own.

He had a mortgage, he had other debts, and he had the responsibility of supporting a family. He was not worried. He still thought of himself as a natural healer, and the opinion was reinforced by Schweninger's regard for his abilities.

He soon had a few chronic cases and saw townspeople in his consultation room. His practice was much like his father's, with the summertime very busy and the winters quiet. He met his financial obligations easily. He had the prospect of a good practice and plenty of opportunity to rest and read in the cold weather. Nevertheless, he became dissatisfied and bored.

Almost from the beginning he was disappointed in his marriage. Perhaps, as he said of himself, his feelings cooled as soon as he was successful in separating two people, but Else was not an ideal wife. When she became pregnant, she became peevish; the pregnancy absorbed her energies so that her two children were almost forgotten. Groddeck, who enjoyed the role of father, became a loving parent to Else's children. Joachim, the son, was five when his mother married again; he always preferred the stepfather to his own father. Ursula, the younger child, was already showing signs of pathology—too docile, too good, fearful, suspicious; she was to spend many of her adult years in mental institutions.

Sanitarium Groddeck had been operating for a year

when Else gave birth to a girl, Barbara, and devoted herself completely to the baby. Strangers often assumed the child was defective, Else's attentions were so overpowering; when Barbara was fully grown she dared not walk down a flight of steps without clinging to her mother's hand.

To distract himself, as he thought, but perhaps rather to find himself, Groddeck began to write. He felt especially lonely. "A yearning is in me: when I am sad my heart cries for my mother and she is not to be found." Was he looking for something to do that would have pleased his mother?

He had always read a good deal; as a child he had so loved Shakespeare that he had acted the roles of Shakespeare's kings, especially Richard III, with a paper crown and a wooden sword, until his brother Karl laughed at him for insisting that Shakespeare had been a German. Now he tried his hand at writing, and sold his first fiction, a serial story, to the *Frankfurter Zeitung*.

Thus at thirty-five Groddeck found a second career. Writing filled the time between patients and occupied him in the long evenings. It did not occur to him that his feeling of vague restlessness might be connected with his practice. Everything seemed to be going well. Maybe his mother had been right—medicine was a trade, literature was an art. As long as he kept writing the unease was forgotten. Idleness was the threat. He saw to it that he had little time to be idle.

5

THE CASE OF FRAU A.

Among the patients in the early days was an elderly woman who first came to Sanitarium Groddeck in 1901. Chronically ill, she stayed on for a while, improved, and went away, to return from time to time for another "course." Frau A. experienced in her treatment the changes in the medical practice of her physician over a period of twelve years.

She had been under treatment in Berlin for several months before she came to Baden-Baden. One of the doctors she consulted had referred to Groddeck in an offhand way. She might try him. He was said to prefer chronic cases. Besides, the air was very pure in Baden-Baden, and the mineral waters could not do any harm.

Frau A. had never been there before. When she was driven through the neat streets she saw rows of houses with signs advertising doctors and cures. Nearly every block had its tags—Sanitarium, Health Pension, Doctor. There was no way of telling which "Doctor" was self-styled, for there were no legal restrictions, and anyone could call himself a doctor. She had been warned by friends that Baden-Baden was a haven for quacks, as were all spas, and she must be careful. Of course, she had ascertained that Dr. Groddeck was a *bona fide* physician, but still she felt uneasy. She had heard stories that he was arrogant and unpredictable, and he was a new-comer, rather young.

She liked the looks of the building before which the carriage stopped. The paint was fresh, the window panes sparkled, and flowers grew about the door. She would see, she decided, she would see for herself.

She was admitted by a reassuringly stolid maid. The entry smelled of furniture polish and roses. The maid took her bag and led her up a flight of stairs to her room. A pale, slender woman followed, looked around the room critically to see that all was in order, dispatched the maid to bring a tea tray, and introduced herself as Fraulein Lina, the doctor's sister.

As she reclined on big pillows on the bed, Frau A. asked many questions. When she heard from Fraulein Lina that Dr. Groddeck had been a special student of the great Schweninger, she was satisfied.

The tea arrived and Frau A. was anxious to have Lina hear her story. She had kidney disease, exactly like her poor, dead mother. She had nursed her mother tirelessly until death mercifully released the sufferer, and later she spared no effort in caring for her ailing father, who also developed kidney symptoms at the end of his life. Now she herself experienced the same dreadful pain and discomfort. Three reputable physicians had failed to help her in the slightest. She had only a faint hope that she would find help here.

Fraulein Lina reassured her that she would get better here. Left to rest with the promise that the doctor would see her in the morning, Frau A. leaned heavily against the pillows, one hand protecting her back where the spear of pain was always poised. Insects hummed in the garden, the tumbling waters of a stream made a soothing, steady sound and she fell asleep. She awakened at dusk and saw shadows on the white wall, great trembling fronds from a tree near the window. A child laughed. Somewhere in the house a tenor voice was singing. Frau A. moved carefully on her pillows to avoid the pain. She breathed contentedly. This was a peaceful, beautiful place; she would take mineral baths, which were probably what she had needed all the while, and she would get well.

At 7:30 in the morning she was awakened by a brisk knocking at her door. A meager breakfast was brought in on a tray. She was barely finished when the doctor arrived.

He was a big man; the room was filled with his presence. His cold blue eyes looked directly at her and silently accused her of being ill. He examined her briefly, and she watched him uneasily. He stood and moved rigidly; his head was shaved and his skull was sunburned; he had large, waxy looking ears. He listened to her story, if silence is really listening. It was plain that he did not care to hear her complaints, but she persisted. At last he told her she might lie down on the bed and then he sat down as though to have a friendly chat.

There was no friendliness in his manner. The first thing he said was that she must be on a restricted diet. She must lose a good deal of weight. She protested, putting her hand over her swollen abdomen. This was not fat, this was bloat, from the illness. If she were to eat less it could only be weakening.

He was adamant. She was much too heavy. She was to take her meals in the dining room and eat nothing except what was served to her. In addition to the diet, the treatment would include mineral baths.

She nodded. In a feeble effort to be conciliatory, she said that she had heard of the beneficial effects of the waters.

He ordered sitz baths and arm baths.

Arm baths? Now she was sure he had not listened to her. She put her hand to her side, and explained about the pain. He was making a mistake. There was no pain in the arms.

Arm baths it was to be. He was inexorable. Also she would have a daily massage. He would give her the massage himself. And she would take regular exercise.

Frau A. appealed to his reason. She explained hopefully that she was nearly seventy years old. She was ill. If you cure the illness and kill the patient, there is no profit in that, is there? She looked for a response from him, but his face did not change. She had taken no exercise for thirty years. Did he really think it wise to begin now?

He did. He gave her a bow, bade her good-day, and walked out.

Frau A. found her heart beating rapidly. She was sick with dismay. Could she leave, this morning, if she chose? Or was she no more than a prisoner in this place? What would happen if she said, "Call a carriage. I have decided to return to Berlin."

She would try the baths once before she left. The attendant assured her she could go any time she wished, but patients at Sanitarium Groddeck never left on their own because everybody improved.

Humorless and literal, the attendant talked as she applied steaming towels to Frau A.'s arms. She admitted that a few patients did die. Of course, some were half dead when they came. One had died on the train. Another had fallen down dead on the doorstep. Other doctors liked to send away their hopeless cases, but not Dr. Groddeck. Naturally he could not do much for the dying but even some of those got better.

Frau A. shook her head. She did not understand. She had kidney trouble. For this he orders arm baths? It made no sense. For kidney trouble, what good could hot towels on the arms do? It was not sensible.

Perhaps it did not seem so, the attendant said, pouring more hot water into the tub in which the old woman sat. But if the doctor ordered arm baths, then arm baths were sensible.

As she rested in her room afterwards, Frau A. waited for her massage. The hot water had had a pleasant effect. A nice massage would certainly do no harm. She was comfortably drowsy when the doctor came in.

A table was brought, and Frau A. was helped to lie down on it, on her back. And then the doctor climbed up and kneeled on her abdomen. He told her to take a deep breath.

She could not even speak. The man was mad! She managed only to gasp.

He waited patiently. He shifted his knees to make his position more steady. Still he waited.

Frau A. tried. She drew a shallow breath. He ordered another, deeper this time. She found strength to take a few breaths, convinced that her only hope of escape was in obedience. He forced six breaths from her before he stood up.

He said carefully that it would be easier tomorrow, and they would do more. He bowed and went out. She rested on her bed for a long time, exhausted, shocked, and amused. Yes, she wanted to laugh. It was ludicrous, this treatment. It was really amusing. The man was a lunatic.

She was angered by the tiny portions of food they served her. The man was trying to starve her, or to weaken her fatally. A slice of bread, a bit of fruit, a cup of tea for breakfast. For the midday meal, a sliver of steamed fish, a boiled carrot, a cup of tea, a sweet wafer. And he ordered her to walk, a mile every day the first few days, later a greater distance. It would serve him right if she collapsed on the path, if she were found unconscious or dead in the woods.

She wrote a factual account to her physician in Berlin, making no comment, leaving it to him to decide for himself what sort of maniac this Groddeck must be. She wrote to a friend, complaining in detail, so that someone close to her would have a written record of her experiences.

In the third week, the friend asked a question in a letter. Since the doctor was mad and the treatment unbearable, why did Frau A. remain?

Why? There were several reasons. A reputable physician

had sent her; she wanted to make sure he would never send anyone else. Besides, at seventy, a decision is not made easily, even a decision to pack a trunk and go home. Finally, what was there for her at home? She lived alone. She was always ill, always in pain. There were other patients here, a dozen or more of them, many congenial people. They often had coffee together in the afternoon. They were agreed that Groddeck's methods were incomprehensible, but his results were good. She wanted to be fair, and to be entirely honest she must admit that she was making some progress. Her abdomen was becoming flat, the bloat had gone, she had begun to pass kidney stones, her back scarcely ached, and she slept, probably because of the wonderful pure air, as soundly as a child.

Frau A. remained at the sanitarium five weeks. She returned to her home twenty pounds lighter, free of pain, and more energetic than she had felt in years. She told everyone about her bizarre treatment, the painful massages, the arm baths, the tyranny of the crazy doctor, and she always ended her account with the opinion that he was mad, quite mad, but he had cured her. She was well.

Many years later Groddeck wrote a paper that described the case of Frau A.

In 1901 an elderly lady came to me for treatment. She complained of continual pains in the back and occasional attacks of abdominal cramp. It was not difficult to diagnose renal calculus, and as the patient was very corpulent and the abdomen hard and swollen, I ordered a restricted diet. In order to change the digestive and circulatory conditions, the patient was given hot sitz and arm baths, and I endeavored by means of abdominal massage and breathing exercises to ease the organs within, and in particular the kidneys. In this connection I should explain that it is my practice in such cases to kneel upon the patient's stomach and tell him to take deep breaths; in this way he is forced to use the diaphragm very energetically in breathing and so to press out the fluid contents of the viscera, the blood and the lymph. The treatment proved successful in this case. Within a few weeks the patient passed a number of stones of varying size, and the pain entirely disappeared.

Not every patient was given the treatment Frau A. received, but hers was in no way unusual, and in every treatment there was one unvarying element—the doctor must be unconditionally obeyed. As Schweninger had demonstrated with Bismarck, the first consultation must establish the absolute dominance of the doctor. Almost all of Groddeck's practices involved some pain or discomfort to the patient, some sacrifices in feeding, unaccustomed exercise. At the same time his patients called him a tyrant and accused him of being unfeeling and pigheaded they sat meekly awaiting the next treatment. Nobody terminated his stay at the sanitarium until the doctor gave permission.

Sometimes the orders were cruel. A patient who could not eat certain foods without nausea was fed exclusively on those foods. A patient who had pain on movement was told to keep moving. A patient who protested, weeping, "If I do as you say I shall surely die!" was told quietly, "It would be better for you to die than to disobey me."

Only with the moribund patient was his attitude different. He considered death nothing; it was dying that was difficult. He never left a patient to die alone, not even an unconscious patient. Nor did he readily admit that death was imminent. Death had to be fought until the last moment. When Lina, in 1903, showed unmistakable signs of heart failure, he did everything he knew to help her, and when he saw that it was hopeless, he sat by her bed for hours, talking of an excursion they would make into the Black Forest on the following day. He had a bag packed for her while she watched. She died smiling at the prospect of an unexpected holiday with her brother. She never had to face the reality of her dying, but he faced it, and when Lina left him, he wept.

A few months later, too late to make his mother proud or his sister happy, his first book was published, *Ein Frauen-problem* (*A Gynecological Problem*). Never translated except for an excerpt, it had a respectable sale in Germany.

He kept busy, and he kept writing, but he began to feel unwell. Soon after Lina's death he noticed that he was developing a goiter. It began with a slight swelling on the left side, then involved the right. He described it:

> ... wildly growing fibrous growths, kernels of a swelling, around which were deposited very loose tissues. Slowly the cores enlarged, as well as the newly-formed tissues, followed by a swelling of the throat triangle as well as of the face. Within a few years the neck size swelled from 39 cm. to 45 cm.

The goiter did not incapacitate him. He continued to write. In 1905 a novel was published, *Ein Kind der Erde* (*A Child of the Earth*), dedicated to "my wife and her children," and thereafter he always had a writing project on his desk. He was writing medical articles as well as fiction, and he repeatedly set aside a novel to finish a paper. For the most part the papers dealt with Schweninger's methods and theories, and he planned a book about him for laymen. Schweninger's fame rested mainly on his cure of Bismarck and on the much discussed obesity cure, but his major thesis—Nature Heals—had not received attention. The book, planned for years, was again and again postponed, first for the novel, later a book-length poem, *Die Hochzeit des Dionysos* (*The Marriage of Dionysus*), which was published in 1906.

In that same year came word that his brother Wolf had died in Berlin, leaving a wife and four young children. Groddeck took on the support of the family. Perhaps the other brothers had too many obligations; as when their father had died, there was "nobody who could or wanted to work" for Wolf's family.

Georg had not been in close contact with his brothers. Bummi admitted, when the younger brother confessed how he had idolized the elder, that he had scarcely taken notice of his childhood existence. Three years after Wolf's death, Bummi died of heart disease. Now only Hans was left of the family, and Groddeck threw himself into greater activity. He became a regular lecturer for a group of laborers in Baden-Baden who had formed a club "for education and discussion." He spoke on whatever concerned him at the moment—protection of natural resources, questions of social welfare, ways to gain strength through unified effort. He read the work of Robert Owen and was optimistic about cooperative movements. He organized a debating society. In odd moments he worked on a critique of Ibsen's plays, *Tragödie oder Komödie* (*Tragedy or Comedy*), which was published in 1910. He wrote a collection of essays, *Hin zu Gottnatur* (*Toward God-Nature*), published the following year. He organized a cooperative society and became chairman of the board.

He still put off the book about Schweninger. He wanted it to be first-rate and he planned to take a long vacation in the winter so he could write the book at leisure. But before he was ready to begin, he underwent a kind of conversion. He made a discovery that changed everything—his practice, his personality, and his future life.

6

THE REALITY OF SYMBOLS

After Bummi died, Groddeck said sadly, there was nobody left to call him Pat. He was depressed, "mentally bankrupt," as he put it. "I felt old, I had tired of everything I used to hold dear, and above all, my work as a physician had become distasteful to me. I pursued it merely for the sake of an income . . . During this time I undertook the treatment of a lady who was seriously ill."

The lady was Fraulein G., a spinster, stricken with more than one ominous disease. She had several times undergone major surgery and arrived in Baden-Baden with a suitcase full of medicines. It was taken for granted by the physician who sent her that she would "soon end her sufferings."

In the usual way, Groddeck visited her on the morning after her arrival. Like all the patients' rooms, hers was plainly furnished with a bed, a commode, a wardrobe, a stove of Dutch tiles, an armchair, a footstool, a small writing table and chair. When he approached the room, Groddeck noticed that the chamber pot and the footstool had been placed in the hall outside the patient's door.

The patient was lying on the bed against a pile of pillows. Her lips were blue, her fingertips dark; she was terribly emaciated and so exhausted from the journey to Baden-Baden that she could scarcely speak.

Because she was patently close to death, he was extremely kind to her. He sat in the armchair and spoke softly. He listened attentively when she struggled to speak. When it suited him he was an excellent listener. Fraulein G. had been to more than one spa, she had been treated by physicians in Berlin and Cologne; she had undergone surgery, she had taken most of the popular "cures." She knew that she was very ill. As she spoke, he nodded and made murmurs of encouragement. He had heard the same story many times. Idly, he flipped the tassel of the antimacassar.

She sat upright and burst into agitated speech, much stronger than she had been capable of producing until that moment. She begged that he stop what he was doing. She simply could not bear it.

He dropped the tassel and said politely that he was sorry he had upset her. A few minutes later he absently pulled at the tip of his nose. She was again upright. Again she begged that he stop what he was doing.

He was at a loss. What other moves were prohibited? He said contritely that he was sorry, but perhaps if she could tell him—what were the other things?

She shook her head. She could not tell until she saw.

He nodded. Self-conscious, he fingered his new watch fob, a gift, in the shape of a miniature skull. One glance at her face and rigid posture and he dropped it hastily. She suggested that perhaps he would like to look at her medicines.

He agreed, relieved to be on a safe subject, and asked where they were. She moved her head in the direction of the wardrobe. As he hesitated, she jerked her head again, to indicate the wardrobe.

Still he waited, although he knew what she meant. She could not speak the word. "The thing for the clothes," she said finally.

She could not bring herself to speak the word "wardrobe." Why not?

He spent a long time with her. He explained that with a new patient it was his policy to discontinue all drugs for a few days. She agreed at once, although her previous physician had warned her that she could not live twenty-four hours without her medicines. He told her that he would see her every day except Monday, which was his day of rest. It pleased her that he did not rest on Sunday. So he was a little peculiar, too? He said he believed he was.

In the course of the conversation, to which he attended with great interest, he learned that there were many words she could not utter. She could not say *stool*, she could not say *stovepipe*. There were objects she could not tolerate near her, such as the chamber pot and the footstool, which had been put out of the room at once. There were gestures people made absently, pulling at the nose, plucking at the ear lobe, twirling a pencil, which put her into an agony of embarrassment. He found it fascinating to try to guess which movements and which words were forbidden.

Much interested, he left her at last. He took away a mental list of words and objects that disturbed her, but without a clue as to their meaning for her. He was not satisfied merely to call her peculiar, even psychotic. To name the problem explained nothing.

There was something else about this woman that was interesting. She had come to the sanitarium accompanied by her sister. The housekeeper reported that the sister was to be present at all consultations and examinations. Yet, when he went to the patient he found her alone. He learned that Fraulein G. had caught a glimpse of him as she entered the sanitarium, that she had been told he preferred to see the patient alone, and without argument, she had agreed. Why was that?

From the beginning, she placed a childlike confidence in him, but her confidence was more than ordinary. Most of his patients regarded him as powerful, rather forbidding, a strict father. Fraulein G. did not look on him as a father; she looked on him as a mother. Oh, come, he told himself, preposterous! There was no evidence for such a notion. He went into his study and looked curiously into the mirror. With his shaved head, the deeply-lined face—a patient had recently asked if the lines were duelling scars—oh, no, he could scarcely be said to have a maternal look.

In the morning, he saw Fraulein G. again. She had had a good night's sleep, she told him gratefully, as though she owed it to him, and now she was ready to undertake any treatment he suggested.

He made an examination. It left her exhausted. He chided himself. The poor woman would not survive many such procedures. He told her that he would order a special diet, that she was to have the baths, moderately warm, and that he would see her again tomorrow. She agreed readily to everything he said, and he left her, more puzzled than before.

The answer did not come all at once. One day he found it merely amusing that she was unable to say the word "stool." Another day he understood that the word meant more to her than "the thing for the feet." After a week he was beginning to understand that a stovepipe, black and rigid, could be frightening, as a pointing finger could be threatening. Gradually he found himself understanding more and more of Fraulein G.'s mental world.

The concept of symbols was not new to him. Literature was full of symbols. But he had never met anyone who lived as though the symbol had the same reality as the external object. Once that reality was grasped, all Fraulein G.'s circumlocutions and prohibitions became logical. Of course, she could not bear to see someone play with a tassel, pluck at a moustache, pull at the nose—that was masturbation. Of course, a heated stove must horrify her. Certainly, a box was a woman. These objects were sexual to her, not symbolical, but real.

Besides the abnormal importance of symbolism in Fraulein G.'s thinking, there was also the puzzling point of her attitude toward him. She had complete confidence in him, which had not been so with any previous physician. She endowed him with all sorts of fine qualities he did not possess, but which had been possessed by loved figures in her past. There was no sense to it; it was as though she concluded that he must be kind because he had blue eyes and her first nurse had been blue-eyed and kind. But what if the nurse had been blue-eyed and cruel? It could just as easily be true.

By the time Fraulein G. left the sanitarium, he understood this phenomenon, too, and she herself, though not cured, was in better health than she had dreamed possible.

He tried the new listen-and-watch game with another patient. To his delight, this patient, too, revealed the power of symbols. As with Fraulein G., the symbols were unrecognized. For example, the second patient was terrified of birds. There was no sensible reason for the fear. She would readily agree that birds were harmless, none had ever frightened her or injured her, she knew that they neither poisoned the atmosphere nor portended evil. But she was terrified just the same.

Another patient was susceptible to terror and nausea at the sight of small animals such as mice and squirrels. Again she knew of no reason. It was simply an abhorrence. Mice, especially, were revolting to her; they had always been revolting. And so it went. Everybody reacted to symbols, but few were aware of their significance.

A woman who feared mice was not considered peculiar; the fear of mice was common in women. Did mice, then, stand for the same thing to all women? Was the mouse a universal symbol? Was there such a thing as a universal symbol? And how was it that he had never noticed the high proportion of women in his practice? Eight out of ten patients were women. There must be a reason for that.

Groddeck was euphoric. Every hour was fruitful, everything he saw or heard gave him a new idea. Some of the ideas

were so startling and so exciting that he wanted to drop everything, sweep his desk clear of all other papers, and write it all
out. It was new, it was absolutely original. He began to note
on paper what he was seeing, what he was hearing, what he
was speculating upon. When he read over what he had written, he gained more ideas.

Certain things struck him as so obvious and true that he
marveled he had overlooked them before. New questions
arose. What was the importance of the attitude of patient to
physician? Why had his ailing father always improved when
the doctor came? What was the power of a feeling? Was there
some sort of unknowing *willingness* to be ill? What was the
real meaning in apparently random movements and habitual
gestures?

For the first time, he looked at himself objectively, and
at Else, his wife, who was no longer in love with him, if she
ever had been. He stared, as though he had been transported
to a foreign country, at everyone around him. He saw that the
human being may express himself more truthfully in his gait,
his facial expression, his hands, the flicker of an eyelid than in
the most heartfelt words.

For months he went on with his observations, testing and
appraising. He was still practicing medicine but his methods
were changing before he quite realized what was happening.
Peremptory orders became questions. Arrogance became diffi-
dence. Consultations became interludes of quiet conversation.
With the old methods he knew exactly what could be accom-
plished. His results had not been negligible. Indeed, his suc-
cesses had been sufficiently impressive to fill his waiting room
with chronic cases. Other doctors were glad to send him their
unresponding cases and their hopeless patients. But even with
these, now, his results became astonishing. He began to gain a
reputation as a wonder doctor. "In his waiting room," wrote
von Roeder, "dukes sat next to laborers. He treated cases
which had been abandoned by specialists from Holland and
England and the Nordic countries."

But the long-postponed book on Schweninger, a moral obligation, still weighed on his conscience. He was going far beyond Schweninger, and he had not yet done justice to his teacher. He took out his notes, set to work and wrote the book quickly.

Entitled *Nasamecu,* from the Latin *Natura sanat, medicus curat* (Nature heals, medicine cures), expressing Schweninger's basic belief, the book was published in 1913. Schweninger had taught that the physician's function was to help set in motion the healing process, and the subtitle was, "The understanding of people in health and disease."

7

TOWARD A NEW THEORY
OF ILLNESS

Nasamecu enjoyed wide popularity but before it had been out many weeks, Groddeck was regretting it. He found himself in the uncomfortable position of hearing his book praised on all sides, not for the premise, Nature Heals, which he considered valid, but for its attack on Freudian psychoanalysis. Compared with the vituperative criticisms then current, the attack was mild, but he considered it unjustified. He had written:

> Especially in recent years the events of daily life and the mysteries of sex are perhaps too eagerly traced. A change in moral laws seems to be taking place, as a result of which nobody can predict whether it will lead to the raising or the decline of mankind . . . The problem in psychoanalysis is to lead back, through exact investigation of the innermost heart, symptoms of all kinds of illness, psychical or physical, to strong psychic experiences which the patient endured in early childhood and which are mostly of sexual character . . . Now psychoanalysts take for their particular task the disclosure of this experience, showing its harmlessness, explaining to the patient the development of his sufferings from his vain attempt at killing thoughts, and curing him in this way. I admit that Freud, the founder of

this movement, has greatly enlarged our knowledge of the mind.

Also, I appreciate the competence and the amazing success of this treatment in special cases and through special doctors . . . Nevertheless, the cases of illness urgently needing such a treatment and when no other treatment could replace it, are rare. Doctors who are sufficiently great, unselfish, and kind, to practice such a treatment without endangering the patient, are still more rare. Once and for all he (the patient) becomes the slave of his doctor, he feels the chains even if he has the courage to move free of them. It needs a strong mind to get free again . . . Even the high-minded of the psychoanalysts cannot avoid this difficulty. And how many are high-minded?

This whole movement has about the same effect as if one took a syringe of morphine and gave injections to every person with pain. Now it is mostly physicians who use the dangerous poison of psychoanalysis. But this will not last long. This practice will not remain in the circle of medical doctors. It will spread like an epidemic, has already spread . . . What a deplorable spectacle it will be if everyone who imagines he has psychological knowledge stirs up the secrets of friends, relatives, or protégés. Everyone will imagine it, because everyone, in the character of father, teacher, tutor, friend or husband is obliged to practice some kind of psychology. It will be as with piano playing. Because two or three great pianists exist, every schoolboy and schoolgirl has to sit at the instrument of torture. But bad piano playing hurts only the ears, the play with psychoanalysis will tear innumerable hearts.

He who has once seen an unhappy patient who has gone through the hands of skilled and scrupulous psychoanalysts without finding healing must ask what would happen in case of bungling. Some people are already so arrogant that they believe they understand all the secrets of thought and poetry because it is now

printed in books that dreams can be explained sexually
and that children know much more of the world than
prudish and blind parents may believe. Man remains
always the same. He discovers a little truth and he
thinks he is a god who understands everything.

Some of Groddeck's misgivings proved justified. Ernest
Jones wrote about untrained people who set themselves up as
teachers of psychoanalysis and put advertisements in English
newspapers offering training courses. Everyone who had
heard the word psychoanalysis had an opinion about it. Gossip, scandal, and misinformation spread rapidly. There were
tales that psychoanalysts prescribed sexual activity as a cure
for melancholia, tics, and skin rashes. As Groddeck predicted,
it was to prove impractical, at the least, to psychoanalyze
every patient. As for the patient becoming the slave of his
doctor, it was nearly true. Freud wrote, "The transference is
altogether a curse," and for a long time, freeing the patient of
the doctor was a serious problem.

Groddeck's statement about "a little truth" is unfortunately still valid. The popular lay view is still widely held,
especially by those who favor simple explanations, that all
creativity can be understood by calling it sublimated sexuality.

What troubled Groddeck about *Nasamecu* was not a
change of opinion—he was to change his mind many times,
without apology—but his embarrassment at having written
without first-hand knowledge. All that he knew about psychoanalysis was what he had been told. He had never read a book
of Freud's.

Yet by the time his colleagues were congratulating him
on his annihilation of psychoanalysis, he himself was using
psychoanalytical methods, which he called "psychical treatment." He found them applicable and useful, in varying de-
grees, to every patient.

Frau A., for example, though she improved considerably

in 1901 with a regimen of strenuous massage, baths, and diet, was only temporarily improved. In his paper on her case, Groddeck wrote:

> The only ground for complaint lay in the fact that from time to time the treatment had all to be gone through again, because new stones were perpetually forming. So things went for twelve years. Meantime I had started to combine psychotherapy with my previous modes of treatment, and to my own surprise had found this of great advantage. When I felt confident of my own technique I decided to apply it to this elderly patient also, and this I did in 1913. From that time until her death from old age in 1925 she never again showed the slightest sign of calculus, so that I think we may assume that it was the psychical treatment which put an end to that proclivity. During the time when I had used physical measures alone she had passed well over a hundred stones.

The search for an explanation of his success with psychotherapy in the treatment of physical disease led him into a new concept of what constituted disease. Illness was no longer understandable to him as a mechanical or chemical dysfunction of organs, but became a creation, a symbol, and it was on this premise that he planned to write a book.

Inevitably, his new outlook affected his personal life as well as his practice. In 1914, after years of estrangement, he finally separated permanently from Else.

He remained on good terms with her children, especially the boy Joachim. Barbara, now thirteen, stayed for a short time with Else and then went to live with friends of Groddeck in Baden-Baden.

That same year Hans, the last of his brothers, died. Now he was truly alone and he made himself as busy as possible.

As chairman of the cooperative society, he projected a cooperative grocery store, which was an immediate success. Remembering his father's unfortunate experience with a building scheme, he instituted one that was entirely different. He founded a cooperative building society, and a group of low-cost houses was built not far from the railroad station at Baden-Baden. The houses are still there today, still occupied.

And then came war. As a trained Army surgeon Groddeck was put in charge of a Red Cross hospital in Baden-Baden. He had in his care more than a hundred patients, officers and enlisted men, and he was able to combine his new methods with the old ones. The results were gratifying.

There was one complication. The official position of the German army toward hospital patients was that most of them were malingering. One day, while Groddeck was away, an investigating committee arrived unexpectedly. The committee members spoke to a few patients, cursorily examined one or two, and arbitrarily discharged several men for immediate duty at the front. Others were ordered removed to hospitals where the surroundings and the treatment would be less agreeable. There were rumors, some later substantiated, that a few of the men were given electric shock in an effort to make hospital life more terrifying than combat.

When Groddeck returned to the hospital and heard of the visit and its outcome, he was outraged. He sat down at once and wrote a furious letter to the commanding general. He did not temper his phrases, convinced that truth would triumph, and perhaps counting on the influence of the Kaiser's sister and brother-in-law, who were his patients. To his dismay, he received a formal communication two weeks later which relieved him of his post. He was no longer needed in the army.

He was reluctant to leave; he had come to regard his patients as children who relied upon him, but there was no recourse. He went around to each bed and wheelchair and said goodbye. With a real feeling of regret, he walked out of the hospital as the patients sang in his honor, "I had a comrade once, you'll never find a better."

The regret did not last long. He returned to the sanitarium and was soon busy with new patients. In June of 1915 he was asked to see a pretty young Swedish widow, Emmy Von Voigt, who was depressed and hopeless about her symptoms. He agreed to see her and to give his opinion, although two physicians had agreed that she should have surgery for intractable uterine bleeding. Various drugs had been used without success, she was dangerously exsanguinated, but she had heard somewhere of Groddeck and she wanted to see him before she underwent surgery. As she described it, "He came to see me and he looked at my records and he looked at me with terrible eyes and said, 'Do you want an operation?' and I said, 'No.'"

She was moved to the sanitarium where he spent a couple of hours talking with her. Suddenly she was fearful, she could hardly bear his eyes. "He looked at me with the eyes of my mother." And whether it was the gaze of her mother or the talk or whatever, the bleeding stopped, the depression disappeared, and in a couple of weeks she was able to leave.

She did not go at once, but rested at the sanitarium and watched Groddeck. She was a masseuse herself, but she had never seen massage like his. She applied herself to learn it and in the winter of 1916 went to Hamburg and worked in a military hospital. In July, 1917, after much correspondence, she returned to Baden-Baden to act as Groddeck's assistant.

Though he still used massage, Groddeck now thought of it as psychotherapy and began to take note of its effects. He had an ardent admirer in his lovely assistant, who, from the first, looked on him as a miracle worker. She never changed her mind, neither during the years they waited for his divorce nor in their exceptionally happy marriage. She never had a doubt about his greatness, and even before her return to

Baden-Baden was urging him to write a book about his new therapy. He had a score of case histories and had made pages of notes. But before he could get on with the book he realized he had a more difficult piece of writing to accomplish.

On May 27, 1917, he sat down and wrote a long letter to Sigmund Freud.

8

GRODDECK AND FREUD—
AN EXCHANGE OF LETTERS

My dear Professor:

First let me send you my warm thanks for all I have
gained through the study of your writings. The need to
express my gratitude becomes a duty, because in 1912
I published a book, passing premature judgment on the
subject of psychoanalysis. The text itself indicates that
at the time my knowledge of psychoanalysis was based
merely on hearsay. That my inexcusable blunder was
owing to ignorance (which by no means mitigates it)
would require no explicit assurance from me, except
that circumstances make the story of my conversion—
if I may use the word—interesting.

In 1909, that is, three years before the publication
of my book, a woman came to me for treatment. My
observation of her forced me into the very path which I
later came to know as that of psychoanalysis. I can
definitely assure you that the patient was ignorant of
the very word psychoanalysis, and I'm almost inclined
to believe the same thing of myself. Through her I
perceived the characteristics of infantile sexuality and
symbolism, and very soon—in a few weeks or so—
stood faced by the concepts of transference and resistance. And though I have just learned the terms trans-

ference and resistance, both became—to a certain degree automatically—pivotal points in the therapy. The joy of discovery sent me into a state of intoxication which lasted several years. Testing the discovery against other therapeutic material and the events of everyday life, this became a period of rich fulfillment for me.

Originally cautious about my views, I found that the more freely I aired them to others, the more often did the name of Freud turn up as the pioneer of this whole sphere of ideas. Because all my life, and despite all experience to the contrary, I had clung to the wishful thought that I myself was creative, I fought against the recognition that once more, in some mysterious fashion, I had merely absorbed and digested another's ideas. So my attack of 1912 proceeded from a kind of premonitory sense of envy.

In 1913 I saw your *Psychopathology of Everyday Life* in a shopwindow and bought it, together with *The Interpretation of Dreams*. The effect of the books was so shattering that, though I knew I was depriving myself of the chance to enrich my knowledge and life immeasurably, I finished neither of them.

Through the following years, because of the time-consuming psychic therapy, the volume of my work increased so heavily that I had to find some way out. I hit on the plan of delivering lectures to the patients in my sanitarium, since this would at least eliminate the necessity of explaining to each individual those basic ideas which I still considered my property. Actually, I achieved my purpose. The impression made was so strong that I planned to revise and publish these extemporaneous lectures. I reached that decision in October, 1916. Feeling obscurely that something was wrong with this apparent discovery of mine, I tackled your books again, then proceeded to concentrate on the study of psychoanalytic literature, insofar as it hadn't been silenced by the war. One of the results of my belated honesty is this letter, whose primary purpose is probably an attempt to justify myself in my own eyes.

The wish persists to publish in some form the results of my long years of labor, but another difficulty remains which has not yet been solved for me. After reading your *Contributions to the History of Psychoanalysis*, I've begun to doubt whether, within your definition of the term, I might count myself a psychoanalyst. I don't want to label myself the follower of a movement if I must run the risk of being rejected by the leader of that movement as an intruder who doesn't belong. Which is why I beg you to give my letter a few more minutes of your time.

It was not through the study of neuroses that I arrived at my views—or should I say your views?—but through the observation of diseases which we are wont to call physical. Originally, I owe my reputation as a physician to my work in physical therapy, specifically as a masseur. Therefore my patients are probably unlike those of a psychoanalyst. Long before I met the above-mentioned patient in 1909, I was firmly convinced that the distinction between mind and body is only a word, not an essential distinction—that the body and mind are a joint thing which harbors an It,* a power by which we are lived, while we think we live. Naturally, I can't lay claim to this idea either, but it is and was the starting point of my activity. In other words, I have refused from the beginning to accept the divorce of bodily and mental ills. I have tried to treat the whole individual, the It in him; I have searched for a way leading into my untrodden, the pathless. I knew that I was moving close to the borders of mysticism, if not already standing in the very thick of it. Still, the plain facts forced me to continue on my way.

If I understand it correctly, psychoanalysis works

* *Das Es*, translated through Groddeck's work as the It.

primarily with the concept of neurosis. I assume, of course, that for you, too, the word covers the whole of human life. In any case, this is true for me. The It, which is mysteriously connected with sexuality, Eros, or whatever you choose to call it, shapes the nose as well as the hand of the human, just as it shapes his thoughts and emotions. It may express itself in inflammation of the lungs or cancer, just as it does in compulsion neurosis or hysteria. And just as the symptomatic activity of the It in hysteria or neurosis calls for psychoanalytical treatment, so does heart trouble or cancer. Differences essential in themselves do not exist which could prompt us to try psychoanalysis here and leave it untried there. Where one calls halt to the psychoanalytical treatment is instead a practical problem, a problem of personal judgment. I use the word treatment, because I don't believe that the doctor's activity extends beyond treatment. He doesn't take care of healing, the It does that.

Here is the point where I begin to doubt whether or not I have the right to set myself up as a professional psychoanalyst. In the development of these ideas, which are basically your ideas, it becomes impossible to use a terminology other than what you have established. There is no substitute for it and it serves my needs, too, once the concept of the Unknown is expanded. But in the *International Journal* you expressly limit the meaning of the Unknown. If one wishes to amplify this meaning—which is essential for the psychoanalytical treatment of so-called physical ailments —one may then be overstepping the limits you have set on the definition of psychoanalysis. In that case I should have to insert a section in the book I plan, trying to untangle my relationship with psychoanalysis —an attempt which would probably be misunderstood.

Nowhere else, in all of his numerous publications, did Groddeck delineate his ideas more clearly, in their initial form. And his difference with Freud on the meaning of the Unknown, which Groddeck was calling the It, was clearly set forth in this letter. The letter went on for pages, with examples from cases, the symptoms, the treatment, the outcome. He put the letter in the mail and went back to work, but he was distracted. He was at one moment sure that Freud would write politely but in a noncommittal way; in the next moment he was certain that the man who had written *The Interpretation of Dreams* would be understanding and encouraging. He tried to prepare himself for an outright rejection. If it came, he would then disassociate himself from psychoanalysis and give Freud credit for such terms as he borrowed from psychoanalysis. He would go on his own way. It really mattered very little whether Freud welcomed him or waved him away.

The letter reached Freud at a time when he was cut off by the war from most of his colleagues. Ernest Jones was in England; Ferenczi, the Hungarian psychoanalyst and close friend of Freud, was in a sanitarium with tuberculosis complicated by Grave's disease; his condition was serious. To Freud, the unexpected and admiring support from Groddeck was welcome, and he was impressed. Here was a thoughtful attempt to restore the concept of unity in man, at a time when the artificial separation of mind and body was the rule in medical thinking. The very advances in science had enhanced the separation—Virchow, Koch, Pasteur had been concerned with the body as an immensely complicated machine. The mind was something entirely separate.

What also impressed Freud in the letter was that Groddeck, working alone, had not stopped at a theoretical formulation but had gone on to treat organic disease by psychological means. This was a giant step forward.

Freud replied promptly. Groddeck's letter had pleased and interested him so much, he said, that he was tempted to disregard conventional courtesy and respond with analytical frankness. He proceeded to do so:

I notice that you urgently petition me to give you official confirmation of the fact that you are not a psychoanalyst, that you are not one of a group of followers,
but rather you claim to be special, individual. I would
apparently do you a great favor if I would reject you,
push you away to where Adler, Jung, and others are
standing, but I can't do that. I must lay claim to you
and must state that you are a splendid psychoanalyst,
whose thorough understanding of the essence of the
matter* is permanent. Anyone who has recognized
transference and resistance as the focal points of
therapy belongs irretrievably to the mad horde. It does
not matter that he calls the unconscious "the It." Let
me show you that it is not necessary to extend the
concept of the "unconscious" in order to include your
experience with organic disorders. In my article about
the unconscious which you mention you will find a
small footnote (page 258f): "We shall save for mention in another connection a further important preroga-
tive of the unconscious." I shall tell you what I kept
back there: namely, the assertion that acts of the unconscious have intense plastic effects on somatic processes in a manner impossible to achieve by conscious
acts. My friend, Ferenczi, who knows about this, has
lying ready in the folder of the *International Journal* an
article about patho-neuroses which comes very close to
your communication.

Freud believed that Groddeck's observations coincided
so beautifully with Ferenczi's speculations that he hoped to
publish an article by Groddeck before publishing Ferenczi's
article. The letter went on to welcome Groddeck's efforts.
Then the tone changed from approbation to scolding.

I am disturbed by one circumstance: that it seems you
have so little overcome the banal ambitions that

* *Die Sache.*

clamor for originality and for priority. If you can be
sure of the independence of your achievement, of what
use can originality be? By the way, can you be sure on
that point? You are surely 10 or 15 or perhaps even 20
years younger than I (1856). Mightn't you perhaps
have absorbed the leading ideas of psychoanalysis in a
cryptomnesic way, similar to the way in which I was
able to explain my own originality? What, after all, is
the worth of the struggle for priority against the older
generation?

Next came praises of the cases Groddeck had described.
One was fascinating, he said. It dealt with a man who suffered
recurring retinal hemorrhage. It was truly a fascinating case,
beautifully demonstrating Groddeck's courage and skill. Such
an example had never been given before. Then the scolding
resumed.

And now to the second consideration! After your beautiful basic premise why do you throw yourself into
mysticism and point out the difference between the
psychic and the physical? Why do you hold firmly to
philosophical theories which are not called for?

Freud's letter ended with a plea for acceptance of the
frankness with which he had written and the assurance that it
was meant in a friendly way. It was in this manner that Freud
was always to write to Groddeck—as a mentor, a guide, the
parent who praises, encourages, cautions and criticizes.

There could have been no more satisfying reply for
Groddeck. He sang aloud. He did a little dance. The scolding
made no matter; every father scolded. He had been accepted.
He belonged. Freud had become for him all the loved ones he
had lost.

9

THE PSYCHOSOMATIC FACTOR

In the happiness Groddeck felt at being accepted by Freud, there remained a small worry. He was tempted to agree with everything Freud said. But Freud said it made no difference whether one called the Unknown, the "It" or the "Unconscious." Groddeck was not so sure. It was not a difference of names for a given concept. It was a difference of concept.

What Freud meant by "unconscious" at this time, though he modified his view later, was that which had been repressed and forgotten. The implication was that all the repressed and forgotten material in the unconscious had at some previous time been conscious. Groddeck's was a much broader concept, and he was so eager to explain this clearly and convincingly to Freud that he composed his next letter with special care. He wrote out a preliminary draft before he penned the final copy.

> I wish to add a few words about the unconscious (the It) . . . There still exists—at least ostensibly, an opposition between the unconscious and the conscious, just as if there were two active forces. Apparently we still consider, even in psychoanalytical circles, a great many outward appearances as pure descendants of the conscious and we act as if the unconscious couldn't pos-

sibly have anything to do with them. I am of the opinion that the conscious is merely a form of expression of the unconscious, that all that happens in human life (animal and plant life don't concern me for this purpose, just as inorganic life doesn't) is created by the unconscious . . . We daren't think that our own actions could be given impetus by a thinking which is apparently outside of the actual inter-relationship of the occurrence; we must think that we always act through a certain inner force empowered by omnipotence, that we are formed and act by it . . . In the final analysis all this is evaluated in the treatment of the patient. And there I have the hypothesis that it is the It which makes man sick because it follows some purpose which it has found useful.

"Apparently we still consider, even in psychoanalytic circles"—how good it was to write that "we," to be accepted. No man was ever so lucky. There was Emmy, who loved him and shared his enthusiasm for his new work, and there was Freud, who was father, mother, teacher, sister, and brothers. It was blissful even to disagree with him. Freud took him seriously, considered his ideas worthy of discussion. He was no longer the "favorite student" he had been with Schweninger, which was after all a subordinate, junior position. Now he was a colleague, something of a grown son.

Freud did not reply to Groddeck's letter until the end of July, 1917, when he wrote from his vacation spot of Csorbató. Ferenczi, recently discharged from the sanitarium, had found the spot and spent two weeks there with him. Hans Sachs, Max Eitington, and Otto Rank also were in Csorbató while Freud was there. The very backbone of the pyschoanalytic movement! They had read Groddeck's letter and heard about him from Freud.

Freud apologized for his slowness in replying, with the explanation that he had sent Groddeck's letter on to Ferenczi and had waited for it to be returned. He said again that he believed the differences in their points of view, his own and Groddeck's, were not crucial. "You should consider yourself as one of those close to us and you should come to assist us in our work. Our periodicals are open to you. We should be pleased to receive contributions from you."

For Groddeck, the invitation opened a whole world. His ideas, even when he had followed Schweninger, had never been popular in medical circles. His espousal of Schweninger's theories, especially the idea that the physician's importance is negligible, was galling to most of his colleagues. The new theory of illness, when he found an opportunity to speak of it, was received politely and dismissed as speculative and unproven. Like Freud, Groddeck was not dismayed by hostile reactions; indeed, he often welcomed them, for he found something suspect in ideas which were too readily embraced. But now, with Freud's acceptance of him, despite their "minor" differences, the psychoanalytical periodicals were open to him. He could publish his views.

From this time, the letters to Freud are reminiscent of those Freud wrote to Wilhelm Fliess. *The Origins of Psychoanalysis*, the letters to Fliess, demonstrate how Freud tried out notions on Fliess, tested theories and speculations. In the Groddeck-Freud correspondence, Freud took on the role Fliess had played for him. Freud praised, agreed, criticized, made suggestions. Groddeck maintained a respectful, even humble attitude. He signed his letters "Your devoted student," "Always your student," "In cordial admiration," but though he would cheerfully delete a paragraph at Freud's suggestion, rewrite an essay entirely, change a presentation, he would not give up an idea. His theory of the "It" was the heart of his work and life. He argued for it tirelessly. He would not then or later change the original concept of the "It" in any detail.

In his tenacity, too, he was like Freud with Fliess. Jones'

biography gives a list of men who were important to Freud in his early development, good friends all, much admired, but all eventually left behind. For the sake of his cherished ideas, Freud parted with Brucke, Meynert, Fleischl, Charcot, Breuer, and Fliess, "all of whom were good friends to him," according to Jones, and who were "idealized" by him.

Groddeck wrote:

> The university . . . gave me three masters to love. First there was the physiologist Dubois . . . The next was Olshausen, the obstetrician . . . And then came Schweninger, of whom I have written so much in love and recognition, Schweninger of the giant hand, bigger than any other mortal hand has ever been, yet firm and tender at the same time . . . Last of all came Freud . . . the memory of that meeting makes me happy whenever I recall it.

As Freud eventually had to leave his beloved teachers when his development passed theirs, so Groddeck, too, had gone past his early teachers. Only with Freud did he maintain contact to the end of his life. And as Freud made Wilhelm Fliess a transference figure, and did so by discussing his intellectual productions, interwoven with associations, in the same way Groddeck used Freud. Both men began self-analysis in their early forties—Freud at forty-one, Groddeck at forty-three.

Groddeck spent his spare time for the next three months working on a pamphlet for the Psychoanalytic Society, to set forth in detail the views he had expounded in his first letter to Freud. When the pamphlet was finished he sent a copy to Freud. There was nothing new in it, he wrote; it was "a repetition of what I have already told you." The pamphlet, *The Psychic Origin and Psychoanalytical Treatment of Organic Disease*, was the first real investigation into what is now called psychosomatic illness. It was never translated from the German.

Much in the article was new and surprising, and even
with the present widespread interest in psychosomatic medicine, some of the statements Groddeck made in 1917 are still
startling and controversial. Many of the ideas are still un-
tested, although for seventeen years Groddeck said over and
over that he did not expect agreement, he hoped only that his
claims would be tested. The hope was only occasionally realized.

Again like Freud, he began the article with an example
of self-analysis. He described a sudden illness. In the middle
of an afternoon of work with patients, he became suddenly
tired, his throat felt sore, and he had difficulty in swallowing.
The symptoms began, he recalled, immediately after he saw a
patient named Dora. He decided that the clue was the patient's name. "It was the word Dora which was associated
with Freud's priority in the theory of the unconscious."* The
recognition of the idea, "that my unconscious, my It refused
to swallow a realization which was unpleasant to me" caused
a remarkable improvement at once.

Had Groddeck left the description at that point, his experience would have made a neat little example of the power
of a feeling to produce physical symptoms: he had been
robbed of the glory of discovery by Freud, Freud had published a case about Dora, the name Dora gave Groddeck fatigue, pain, and difficulty in swallowing. How marvelous! But
he did not stop there. The article went on to say that later in
the day all the symptoms returned. The following morning
they were worse.

> Only then did I start on my association experiment.
> The inflammation now receded quickly and within a
> quarter of an hour of analysis it was reduced to a thin
> red line going crosswise along the gums. This remnant

* *Fragment of an Analysis of a Case of Hysteria,* the famous case of
Dora.

was lost during the course of the evening. What was
new that this analysis brought to light? It was determined that the battle between the known and the unknown was not about the words Dora–Freud, but
about the words Charlotte–Scharlach, which means
scarlet fever. Immediately before I spoke to Dora, a
child by the name of Lotte was shown to me with a
rash. For the first few moments I considered it the rash
of scarlet fever, and with that conclusion it could be
proved that the sudden fatigue was not, as I first believed, from the word Dora, because it started in the
pause between Charlotte and Dora. In my life, as with
a whole row of my relatives, scarlet fever played a
great and ominous role, and the thought haunted me
that I would some day die from the never-to-be-over-
come consequences. The rejection of the unconscious
was directed in the first place against the death-thought
association with Charlotte–Scharlach, which was
tightly bound up with the complex of vanity, incapacity, or impotence of Dora–Freud. The crux, therefore,
was the word *Schuld*, which means guilt. It occurred
several times in the afternoon in my talks about mort-
gages, money, and money exchanges, in connection
with the cooperative building society. A vivid guilt feeling, which was augmented by the physical processes of
puberty, was present in me at the time of my illness
with scarlet fever and this came out plainly in the analysis. There are obviously still remnants of this although I am now consciously convinced of the ineffec-
tuality of my feelings. In a manner well known to me
(that possible chemical processes can be compared to
the *statu nascendi*) the rising remnants, with the psychic gifts of the Dora–Freud complex, were mixed
and therefore determined the eruption and the strange
remission of illness after my first attempt to analyze
myself. To this discussion of a simple case history I
should add a few remarks. First, from this tale what is
apparent is that neither the psychic condition of the

disease nor its cure by psychoanalysis are clearly determined. That other factors were involved in this inflammation is clearly understandable. The chain of
causes cannot be seen by any single event. One can
only indicate the links of the chain which seem the
most obvious. If we speak of the causes of disease or
even of a causal treatment we must be aware of the
fact that we probably shut out our better pure human
understanding.

It was partly this uncertain attitude of Groddeck's which
annoyed his medical colleagues. The aim of the times was
scientific exactitude. This cause, that effect. Koch bacillus,
tuberculosis. Having nicely demonstrated an emotional cause
for an illness, followed by a psychological cure for the illness,
Groddeck destroyed the argument with the statement that we
cannot know exact causes of illness or cure. The article went
on to discuss causes:

> If one assumes that any illness was the result of infec-
> tion, then the problem has merely been postponed and
> enlarged. The question then arises whether man can
> become susceptible to infection by the changing proc-
> esses between his conscious and his unconscious—a
> question which I answer in the affirmative.
> Just as the It affects the senses, it also affects the
> digestive processes, the distribution of blood, the activ-
> ity of the heart—all in all, the total organic life of the
> personality is being constantly changed. In the same
> manner this It protects itself against the threat of all
> chemical, mechanical, and bacterial attacks, and by the
> same token it may, when illness seems advisable, pro-
> duce conditions in which the pathological germ can be
> permitted to be effective.
> I consider it a basic and dangerous misconception to
> suppose that only the hysteric has the gift of making
> himself ill for whatever purpose. Every man has this
> ability and each uses it in an extension beyond compre-

hension. The hysteric, and in lesser degree the neurotic, force the observer to conclude that in being ill a distinct purpose is served.

Forty years later, Dr. Leo Rangell and others offered this very concept and suggested separation of the phenomenon of conversion (of emotions to symptoms) from hysteria proper.

> To advance at this point the view which is being propounded in this communication, its center is that the process of conversion must perforce be divorced from the concept of hysteria, enabled to stand on its own, and assessed more clearly and from a wider vantage point with regard to its basic mechanism, functions, and borders.
> . . . These somatic changes, in keeping with the original definition and description offered by Fenichel, speak symbolically and via body language express a combination of the forbidden instinctual impulses as well as the defensive forces which bring about the distortions.

Groddeck's pamphlet dealt at length with symptoms and their meanings. Headaches he declared to be "the most widely used means of the unconscious for the halting of thought and drive." The symptoms of a common cold he listed as a reaction against "the evil smell of a word or thought." In children and during the years of puberty "the tonsils are the always-wakeful shepherds of the sensitive soul. Contrarily the mucus membranes of the air passages remain sensitive during the entire lifetime." People who begin the day with coughing, as he himself did, since his army days, "put aside the impressions of their dreams and blow away the intertwined small and great fear fantasies and embarrassments of the coming day." He believed that "the feeling of infirmity can often be eliminated or considerably improved when one asks one's self the question, 'What purpose could the symptom serve?' "

It is in this area that the modern psychosomaticists pounce upon Groddeck's arguments. Symptoms brought about by emotional factors, they say, are not accessible to conscious influence. The patient is unable to answer the question, "What purpose could the symptom serve?" Groddeck, and soon enough Ferenczi, believed that the question could be answered.

> The unconscious answers with a surprising precision, maybe a sore throat to force whispering of secrets, pain in the arm to ward off a tendency to forcefulness or thievery, halitosis to keep the suitor at a distance, cold hands to hide hot emotions, etc. A great many miraculously easy cures which we credit to suggestion or to the personal influence of the doctor are basically to be led back to the sudden realization of the It that man will no longer need this or that protection.
>
> The thought that one could conversely, through physical interference in the material of the It, change the body of man, to lead him from disease to health or vice versa, only sounds strange, but has been known as long as the world has been in existence . . . Both processes finally result in the same thing . . . Amputation of limbs is not a curative process, but the reaction of the unconscious to the amputation is a change in its powers and an effort to try to bring the diseased organism back to life through suffering. Only he who has realized that it is not the operation which heals the leg and furthermore the man—that is a view which seems easy but is in truth very difficult—that a direct cure is never brought about through our medical activities but always through completely unknown healing factors which have been set in motion—can then realize that the objective of the treatment cannot be to heal through our art like magic, but to release unconscious forces.

I am prepared that my communications even with psychoanalysts—maybe not with all—will cause estrangement, let alone with physicians, who, as happened to me previously, have been incorrectly instructed about Freud's teachings . . . To me, it was important to say as clearly as possible that limiting psychoanalytical treatment to the field of neurosis does not give enough knowledge of the workings of analysis. That is, the border is too tight.

Psychoanalysis may not and will not stop before organic suffering. How far its power will extend we shall see.

10

THE FIRST PSYCHOANALYTICAL NOVEL

If Groddeck's article were published today in a medical journal it would probably evoke the same general reactions as it did more than forty years ago, although some of his claims are rather old-fashioned. The "progressive" physician now accepts the argument that emotions and conflicts may be represented by physical symptoms, though often the theory is accepted while the practice is to behave as though it had never been discovered.

The medical student still begins his training in a laboratory, then with a cadaver, and in certain universities does not examine a living patient until his senior year. Many physicians, faced with complaints for which no specific organic cause can be found, order more and more tests in the belief that there must be some obscure physical disorder. Others label the mysterious symptoms with various titles, usually derogatory. This illness is "nervous," that pain is "emotional," "functional," even "imaginary." Every day in the year people are told patronizingly that "there is nothing physically wrong." The sympathetic physician, though he may privately believe a given illness is "in the head," usually prescribes a sedative or a tranquillizer. These men, at least, recognize that though the illness is "only psychological" the pain and discomfort are real.

Many doctors now accept the idea that emotional stresses do cause physical symptoms, but few accept the corollary that a symptom may be the expression of an unconscious conflict of wishes. As for Groddeck's claim that the processes can be reversed—the notion actually offends many graduates of good medical schools. They have peered at bacteria with the microscope, they have dissected their cadaver, they have memorized the names of the cranial nerves. They have seen the demonstrable results of organic disease—changes in tissue, destruction of cells. They can accept, to a degree limited by their observation and experience, the theory that all this might be set into motion by the feelings, but they cannot admit the possibility of healing processes being set into motion by the feelings. A given virus *causes* a given disease, they say, but thousands of people harbor that virus and are well. What, then, causes the virus to become active so that one falls ill? Physicians, teachers, parents all fall back on the phrase "lowered resistance," which illuminates nothing and merely describes what has happened.

The same state of affairs existed in 1917. Perhaps the times were less propitious for a Groddeck then, but Freud found the pamphlet "most interesting and full of meaning," even as he predicted mixed reactions from his colleagues. He urged Groddeck to prepare further papers with more case histories. One other psychoanalyst received Groddeck's paper with enthusiasm, Sandor Ferenczi, whose review appeared in the *Journal* in due course.

> Dr. Groddeck in this pamphlet is the first to make the courageous attempt to apply the results of Freud's discoveries to organic medicine, and this first step has already led him to such surprising results, new points of view, and fresh perspectives, that at least the heuristic value of the step appears beyond any doubt. We

have therefore no justification whatever for rejecting out of hand anything from Groddeck's statements which might startle us now. What he describes is mostly not hypothesis, but fact. He reports that in a great number of purely organic illnesses, such as inflammations, tumors, and constitutional anomalies, he has succeeded in demonstrating that the illness has developed as a defense against unconscious "sensitivities," or that it is in the service of some other unconscious tendencies. He has even succeeded through psychoanalytical work, that is, through making such tendencies conscious, in improving, even curing very severe organic illnesses such as goiter, scleroderma, and cases of gout and tuberculosis. Groddeck is far from assuming the role of a magician, and he states modestly that his aim was merely to create, through psychoanalysis, more favorable conditions 'for the It by which one is lived.' He identifies this 'It' with Freud's unconscious.

Well, he did not *quite* identify it with Freud's unconscious, and Ferenczi had read the letter to Freud in which Groddeck tried to explain the distinction. In the pamphlet the terms were used as though they were interchangeable.

Ferenczi, who was often considered to be hypochondriacal, was even more excited than his review indicated. Here was someone who cured tuberculosis, a disease which had hospitalized Ferenczi for months. Always receptive to new ideas, he was fascinated by the new theory. He wanted to meet this Groddeck face to face.

There was another reason for Ferenczi's temperate tone in the review. Although the *Journal* was a technical publication for psychoanalysts, it was widely read by laymen. Reporters, novelists, and short-story writers scanned it as a source for essays and fictions, and much sensational journalism had been inspired by *Journal* articles.

Ferenczi's hope of meeting Groddeck was not to be realized for some time. Though Groddeck and Freud scarcely took notice of the war in their letters, in 1917 war was a harsh reality. According to Jones, it was at this time that Freud ran out of cigars and developed a painfully swollen palate. When he received a gift of cigars and began to smoke he noticed that the swelling and pain disappeared miraculously. He wrote to Ferenczi and described the incident. Had it not been so striking, he would not have believed in the coincidence. "Quite *à la* Groddeck!" he said.

The friendly reception by Ferenczi, and, more important, by Freud, came when Groddeck was standing alone for the first time, no longer imitating either his father or Schweninger. He had learned to argue in defense of his ideas, but he was not entirely comfortable without approval. He wanted Freud to know everything about him—his theories, his writing, his work with patients, even his daily routine. His wish was to secure Freud's full acceptance. Freud need not consider him correct at all times, but he must accept him with his mistakes and his faults.

Long, frequent letters were exchanged. Nearly every letter contained some reference to the It and the Unconscious. Groddeck continued to insist that his It was necessary to the understanding of his work, that the Unconscious was not broad enough, and Freud stubbornly repeated that the Unconscious was sufficient and that Groddeck was seeking to involve unwarranted philosophical notions.

Later in the year they began a lively discussion of Ibsen. Groddeck's slim volume on Ibsen had been published in 1910; Freud's essay on *Rosmersholm* came out in 1915 and was an examination of guilt in the character of Rebecca West. They disagreed completely in their view of the character and argued with a good deal of heat. Groddeck insisted that Rebecca's confession was fictitious. There was a rapid exchange of letters, with Freud and Hans Sachs taking the position that Rebecca was confessing real guilt. The quarrel was of the sort one might expect from two members of the literature department of a university. In one of his letters on the subject of Rebecca, Freud wrote as an afterthought that he had seen a patient with multiple sclerosis who wished "psychological treatment." Freud asked whether Groddeck would see her. He remarked that she had little money and must know in advance how much the treatment would cost.

Groddeck replied with a continuation of the argument.

> About Rebecca West, you certainly think the same as you did before. I am curious as to how you would explain that Rebecca eavesdrops on Kroll and Rosmer and that she lets it be understood that she knows who has written the anonymous letters. Ibsen was much too careful in his work for one to assume that he simply interjected all this for the fun of it. I have found that after each of Ibsen's works one encounters new material for new problems, both aesthetically and psychoanalytically.

He went on, as casually as Freud had referred to her, to accept the patient and to give detailed costs of treatment. He signed himself, "Your devoted student," and did not write again for two years.

They were good years. Though conditions in Germany were difficult, he was busy and his reputation was growing. He wrote every day, though his patients occupied much of his time. In 1918 he began to publish a little magazine which was circulated within the sanitarium and among a few friends. There were occasional outside contributors, but Groddeck did most of the writing himself. The magazine was called, from a patient's joke, *Satanarium*, and many people continued to call the sanitarium the Satanarium Groddeck.

He was also writing a novel, the first psychoanalytical

novel. He wanted to present a leading character who would personify the unconscious. The man was to behave in an un-civilized, even a psychotic way, and the story was to show how this behavior affected the people around him. Thomas Weltlein, the hero, acted on all his impulses and said anything that occurred to him, an *enfant terrible* who shouted what was usually unspoken.

When the book was finished Groddeck sent it off to a publisher and waited for acceptance. He had never experienced the slightest difficulty in publishing his writings, and although this book was unlike anything he had previously written, he considered it well done and worthwhile. He was completely unprepared for its reception. The publisher was shocked and offended, used the word "salacious" and promptly sent back the manuscript. Groddeck shrugged and sent it off again. Half a dozen publishers who had previously urged him to submit his work announced themselves uninterested in this novel. He rewrote certain passages, re-read the whole, was satisfied, and sent the manuscript off again. It was useless. Everything that seemed of value to him about the book was unacceptable to publishers, and the sections he considered the least successful were highly praised.

His favorite fantasy, in which he sent a handsomely bound copy of his book to Freud, had to be put away with other dreams. In October, 1919, he wrote to Freud and told him what he had been doing.

> Under separate cover I am mailing you a manuscript which I have called, in a spirit of levity, A *Psychoanalytical Novel*. The book has made the customary rounds of publishers and they have regularly returned it to me with most courteous expressions of thanks. I have given up hope of finding someone to publish it, but I would like to have you look at it before it definitely disappears. Perhaps Ferenczi would also enjoy looking through it; I would be happy to express my

thanks through a few gay hours for his kind criticism of my pamphlet.

In my small town isolation I hear nothing of what is going on. My wishy-washy book dealer maintains that *Imago** and the psychoanalytic periodical have become defunct. Is this true? I became so used to this great pleasure, but have not received a copy for months.

The manuscript was mailed to Freud, who failed to acknowledge it. Groddeck went from resignation to depression. He was sure the silence meant disapproval. Probably the book was as bad as the publishers said. Freud was probably disappointed and hesitated to say so.

When he could stand the silence no longer, Groddeck wrote to Freud again. He gave as an excuse the possibility of interesting a new publisher. "The book seems to create displeasure everywhere," he said bleakly. "At least, I interpret your silence as a sign of the same kind of displeasure." But he had written several articles in the past few months on a wide range of topics, from Moses to Struelpeter. "If you could use them for *Imago* I would be glad to send them to you, but perhaps you have things like that in great numbers." He ventured to enclose one article for Freud to read.

Freud replied promptly. "Your contribution arrived. It is just as full and original as your other things. If you like I can confirm all the main points in this from my own experience." What was even better, he was eager to have it used in *Imago* and added, "I hope it is only the forerunner of other contributions."

Freud went on to express his sympathy for the difficulty of finding a publisher for the novel. He said ironically that it might be the title, with the nasty word "Psychoanalytical" that caused antagonism; perhaps Groddeck might find a publisher if he chose a "less scurrilous title." As for himself, he liked the book very much.

* The journal for non-medical articles on psychoanalysis.

Your gift of plastic presentation, which is not at all usual, I admired especially in the train scenes. Naturally I agree with you that the book will not be to everyone's taste. So many clever, free-thinking, and ebullient thoughts cannot easily be digested all at once. And still you ought to try to have it published. Really, there have been worse productions published under the aegis of psychoanalysis. Your contributions to *Imago* will always be welcome to us.

Groddeck's hopes, raised by the possibility of the psychoanalytic society's printing the book, were dashed by the last line of Freud's letter. "At the moment we do not have paper."

The manuscript went out again. It was returned. It went out. It came back. While he waited to hear the latest excuse for rejection, Groddeck thought about the novel and tried to see a way to make it less shocking.

It was useless. He liked it as it was. Emmy liked it. Freud liked it. He went back to articles, wrote up a case study and sent it to Freud, and on April 2, 1920, he told Freud that the novel was still unsold.

Unfortunately I still can only report about the novel that it was once more returned to me. The refusals are not explicit; they always start with great praise of the first part and end with the judgment that the psychoanalytical part destroyed the work of art and therefore the whole has become unusable. The last publishing house even maintained that I got lost in sheer naturalism. I will continue to peddle it. It has given me great courage that you have returned to the work in your last letter.

A little later he said wearily, "I haven't much hope. Everyone who reads it somehow or other bumps against his own repressions and then the opposition begins."

Freud was sympathetic. "If we had money and paper," he wrote, "our publishing house would bring an end to the far-flung travels of your novel." But the publishing house had never made any profits. The only books which had made money had been Freud's, and he never took the money, but left it to help in the Verlag's ever-present financial difficulties.

Groddeck sent a new article to Freud, a case study. Freud was certain that he recognized the patient. It seemed hardly possible that there could be two such people. If he had guessed right, he wanted Groddeck to make some deletions for the sake of discretion. Groddeck might change the occupation, the age, some minor but too-revealing details.

Groddeck admitted that the guess was correct, and made the suggested changes. He was full of ideas for new articles, but before he could throw himself into serious work on them he had to try them on Freud. He wanted to write, from the point of view of a Protestant, an article on the psychoanalytic meaning of the crucifixion. What did Freud think? The letter concluded on a personal note.

> I would like to tell you many more good things; for example, that I am once more sitting among your books and that I am enjoying them. And it is most pleasing to me that there is a man in Vienna who is concerned about me without knowing me . . . Would it please you if I tried to be accepted into one of the psychoanalytical associations? I don't quite fit in, that I know for sure, but I could say that I am easy to get along with.

Freud's reply praised the rewritten article, the "to me so-valuable article," which had already been sent on to the editors of the Journal. He talked of the possibility of publishing the novel at Groddeck's expense, and detailed the costs, which were considerable. "Please give me pleasure with the news that such amounts are of no importance to you!" He was also of the opinion that the title should be changed, even for publication by a psychoanalytical publisher. He believed a title was important. Perhaps it would be better to use as the title the name of the hero, *Thomas Weltlein*, and then they might use as a subtitle, *A Psychoanalytical Novel*.

Freud then had to say something about the embarrassing question of Groddeck joining a psychoanalytical society. The plain fact was he was not welcome. Ernest Jones, who had not met him but had read his articles, regarded him then and forever after as "an amusing oddity." Some of the others, who had waited years for the movement to gain a degree of respectability, were made uneasy by the exuberance and extravagance of Groddeck's written style. Freud knew that there was a likelihood of Groddeck's application being rejected. He showed himself, as he was to do many times in their uneven correspondence, kind and understanding.

He evaded delicately. "Would we gain anything by your entering the Berlin group? I think we could meet at the next Congress (the next one is in The Hague on September 8th)."

But Groddeck had determined to apply. He had no thought of gaining anything for himself, but he was sure he would be pleasing Freud. He made application and when he wrote to Freud again he told him he had applied. There is no way of learning exactly what happened, but the rumor was that Freud used his influence on the Berlin group and Groddeck was accepted.

The letter of acceptance arrived in July, and Groddeck wrote to Freud to tell him. "It would be wonderful to meet you some time," he said, "and The Hague is not unreachable for me."

> For years it has been in my mind to ask you to spend a few weeks with me as a most welcome guest, but one has to bring one's self to ask a thing like that before one dares. But one may harbor wishes.
>
> *Thomas Weltlein, A Psychoanalytical Novel,* that is very simple and good. Many thanks. That you might accept the novel eventually for publication is so pleas-

ant to hear that I cannot be sufficiently overjoyed. The question of money can be solved, not from my means, but I do have friends in Holland who would help . . . I can count on a few hundred marks out of my own circle of acquaintances, so that the loss for the investor would even at worst not be too great.

Travel was somewhat easier than it had been, and, though money was worth little, Groddeck managed to finance the trip for himself and Emmy. He longed to see Freud face to face.

11

THE WILD ANALYST

Freud greeted him so warmly that there was a certain amount of envy from the others. Many of them had been through difficult times with Freud and with psychoanalysis, and it was not altogether pleasing to see Groddeck, a Johnny-come-lately, received like an old friend. Besides, he was accompanied by a woman not his wife. It was too much.

The first congress since the war was well attended, with 119 members and guests. During the four days of meetings, many important papers were delivered, and the days were crowded. On September 9, 1920, the second day of the congress, Freud spoke, followed by several others, and later on the same day, the last speaker was announced—Georg Groddeck. He had not prepared a talk; apparently it was at Freud's suggestion that he was invited to deliver a few words on the subject of his pamphlet.

He mounted the platform, looked challengingly at the audience, and said exactly the wrong thing.

"I am a wild analyst."

There was a stir. Wild analysis, that is, analysis by untrained persons, was a real problem. As early as 1910 Freud had written a paper about the dangers. As Groddeck had predicted in *Nasamecu*, everyone fancied himself an analyst;

all sorts of quacks called themselves such. Anyone who had read a paper on technique could set up shop as a psychoanalyst. There were no diplomas, no certificates necessary. It was to take years before standards of training were established in the large cities of the world.

It was typical of Groddeck's future relations with the official psychoanalytic society that his first public utterance should be tactless. And then the speech itself alienated a good many listeners. Anna Freud was offended by the rambling, unorganized remarks. As she recalled The Hague Congress, Miss Freud admitted that she was shocked by Groddeck. She was then very young and much less tolerant than she became twenty-five years later when she was asked what she remembered about Groddeck's talk and his appearance at The Hague. He did not read a prepared paper, but merely stood on the platform and gave a demonstration of the process of free association, rambling from one idea to another. She was unable to understand why he chose to speak in that way. Obviously he was unprepared, but he made no attempt to put his remarks into any sort of organized form.

There were several possible explanations. He had somehow learned that he was unwelcome in the official organization, and that it was only on Freud's insistence that he was accepted. But even if he had not known, he would probably have been unable to resist shocking his contemporaries. He thoroughly enjoyed stirring people up, making them angry, stimulating them to argument.

He had listened to several papers, some of them excellent, but he was disturbed and bored by certain features of the congress. The only unmitigated pleasure he had experienced was in meeting Freud. Everything and everyone else was disappointing. He was playing "naughty boy" on the platform; and Freud, in the audience, had been unknowingly cast in the role of father; the other members were siblings. He gave them something to cluck over. Jones was coldly amused. Some of the others dismissed him as a crank.

A few of those present were interested and impressed. Otto Rank, Ernst Simmel, Ferenczi, and Karen Horney were delighted at his candor and his refreshing simplicity.

The substance of the talk was Groddeck's thesis that emotional problems are often expressed in organic disease and can be treated with psychoanalysis. His most startling claim was that visual difficulties *always* expressed emotional conflicts. He said that myopia, presbyopia, retinal bleeding, and organic changes in the eye, all were efforts to defend against forbidden wishes *and* to express them. This was too much for most of those in the audience. Ernst Simmel, listening intently, adjusted his thick-lensed spectacles and smiled. The eye, said Groddeck, is the I. (In German, there is no homonym). Visual problems are always caused by the effort of the It to repress the sight of what is painful.

After the talk, Freud sent Groddeck a questioning note. He was amused rather than offended at the manner of delivery, but he was puzzled as to whether Groddeck had been serious at all or merely joking at the expense of the audience. While still at The Hague, Groddeck wrote an answer. He had not exaggerated for effect. He believed that the eye was the most commonly used organ for the expression of emotional difficulties. He had persuaded Emmy, who was slightly near-sighted, that she no longer needed glasses, and she had put them away forever.

The letter to Freud explained his theory more clearly than had his remarks on the platform.

> Your question whether I was serious about my announcement to the congress has followed me around. I will try to make myself understood.
>
> If one asks so-called healthy people to look around at the objects in their living room, then to close their eyes and name the objects, they will regularly leave out this or that object.
>
> If one analyzes why certain visual impressions did not come to the conscious level, it is seen that they

belong to the complex of repression. Thus, there exists a waking censor.

In case the repressed complexes are too much for the strongly visually-inclined person, this censor will become more acute and the eye will become myopic. In case that isn't enough, the unconscious destroys the retina.

This is the same process as in another field, such as the formation of anti-toxin for the overcoming of toxins, just as fever and pus formation are for the over-coming of infections. When the repressions are dissolved, then the censor will become milder and the bleeding in the retina may be given up.

Ceteris paribus: When are you coming to Baden-Baden?

Always your devoted Groddeck

Satisfied that he had made himself understood by Freud, the only person who really mattered, he returned to Baden-Baden and resumed work. He thought back on the congress, and, realizing the poor impression he had made, he began to feel uncomfortable. The other members, with their fraternal attitude, had made him aware that he was an outsider. There was another aspect of the meetings that he disliked, a certain pomposity, a respectable smugness he considered out of place among psychoanalysts. He had over-estimated psychoanalysts, expecting too much from them, expecting, in fact, the grand candor and quality of maturity he had found in Freud. Besides, he was annoyed by their elaborate vocabulary. "Hostility," "resistance," "oral fixation"—too many words used too glibly.

Groddeck tried to ignore his misgivings. He had met Ferenczi, who was easy and friendly, and Rank, who had read the novel and said flattering things about it. The *Verlag* was going to publish it after all and it was to come out in a few months. He had also met a young psychoanalyst who talked at length about "anal erotism." After listening silently for some time, Groddeck shook his head and sighed. "Young man," he said, "you speak of anal erotism. Tell me, have you ever seen an anus?"

The question summed up his feelings about most of the members. They talked too fluently, too easily, in their private technical vernacular, and he could not put down the thought that some of them spoke of things they did not understand.

The point was well taken. Even at this late date, in meetings and congresses, one hears physicians and psychoanalysts using terms as ends in themselves. Thus "the patient demonstrated resistance," is a common phrase, with no tacit agreement as to whether the word "resistance" is used to mean unconscious resistance or a patient's temporary hostility, or his unwillingness to accept an interpretation, or even failure of the patient to progress to the analyst's satisfaction.

Twenty-eight years after Groddeck's complaint, Theodor Reik made a similar observation. In *Listening with the Third Ear*, he lamented the over-use of what he termed Psychoanalese.

> I am afraid of the ease and facility with which they put labels on very complicated human developments. Such throwing around of technical terms can conceal a void full of pretensions. It can easily be confused with a penetrating comprehension of unconscious processes. It can lead to a false show of knowledge that remains peripheral. It can seduce a man into thinking in psychoanalytic clichés and in terms of a card-index science instead of one of personal experiences. . . . Terminology can be a fatal menace to a science if it is used, not to give names to relations, but as a substitute for real comprehension. Its use seduces us to intellectual laziness, so that we substitute something learned by rote for something experienced, something easily acquired for something really our own. I tremble for the new generation, which makes such short work not only of its experiences but also of the analytic terms that describe them. To speak Psychoanalese fluently does not mean to understand psychoanalysis, and a man

who can use all the technical terms correctly can be a very poor psychoanalyst. . . . Followers and pupils of Freud's found new Greek and Latin words in the dictionaries and enriched the psychoanalytic vocabulary. Later some of these technical terms, not understood or misunderstood, found their way into wider circles of educated or interested persons. A new language, *Psychoanalese*, was born. Firmly established by 1920, it has flourished for the past twenty-five years.

Groddeck was similarly concerned in 1920, and soon after he returned to Baden-Baden he wrote frankly to Freud.

> The congress had a somewhat disagreeable result for me. The old experience that the word inhibits the thought has proved itself to me to such an extent that reticence in the face of technical terms—yes, before every delimited definition became still greater.

At the same time, he wrote that he had enjoyed the congress for the opportunity of meeting people. Rank had been friendly and had suggested an excellent title for the novel, *Der Seelensucher* (*The Seeker of the Soul*), which Groddeck liked very much, though he would not use it without Freud's consent.

The congress had been an unforgettable experience for him, he said, because he had finally seen Freud. He had spent the days

> constantly running behind you in a foggy state, much like someone in love, and when I think back I am happy that I am still young enough to feel greatly when it is worth it. My longing is to be together with you quietly, but the prospects for that are not favorable. I sit here, I am tied to this place, and I must make money, and probably it isn't much different for you.

There was one other consequence of the congress, which he went on to mention. His dissatisfaction with the termi-

nology of psychoanalysis, which he feared served too often for
obfuscation, made him long to write something in simple
words. He wanted to explain psychoanalysis to educated laymen who did not have the vocabulary of specialists. It could
be done with a few basic definitions. He told Freud of this
plan:

> With this I come to a matter which I have already
> mentioned a number of times. For many years now I
> have been brooding about a book which should explain
> quietly and fully what I think. I think I will lock myself
> up for a few months during the winter and finish this
> work. I am afraid you won't particularly like it because
> it will contain much mysticism and much fantasy . . . I
> appear to myself like a child of whom one supposes
> that he has been good, while secretly he is planning
> things of which he knows the parents will not approve.
> Because of that I would like you to be acquainted with
> this work. It will decide whether you will still bear with
> me as a follower.
>
> I realize that behind this fear of losing your ap-
> proval lies the wish to be free once again. But this wish
> will have no influence upon the work . . . Perhaps, also,
> I am mistaken and the book won't be quite so danger-
> ous. At any rate, I beg of you not to make a final
> decision about me yet, as far as my medical activity is
> concerned, and as a human being you will not be rid of
> me because I will not let you go. I have grasped very
> firmly, so that it would cost me a piece of my hide if I
> were shaken off.
>
> I hope that my declarations of love do not suffer
> from monotony. Basically I am quiet about it since I
> have seen your understanding smile . . .

With the letter he sent along an article for the *Journal*.
Freud praised the article, which was planned for early publication, but qualified the praise:

Laughingly I noted that at the end of your fine, original article, which was so pleasantly touched by a free kind of skepticism, you have become dogmatic and fantastic and took our mutual, undefined, and easy-running unconscious and gave it all sorts of positive qualities which grew out of a secret source of self-realization.

It was the old disagreement again. Freud's letter went on, indulgently, "Well, every intelligent man has a certain border where he begins to become mystical . . ."

He was strongly tempted by the invitation to visit Baden-Baden for "a more extended exchange of ideas between the two of us." But it was quite out of the question.

Your resigned postscript is quite right. I am in the same position as the Sybil who wanted to sell the last third of her store of wisdom more expensively than the whole thing. I, too, am so impoverished that I have to sell the last of my working time and strength very dearly. Fortunately it is no longer a third. The analogy reaches also that I do not encounter any kings, which have become so rare. I make it all from shopkeepers and other collectors of curiosity.

As to the proposed book, Freud said he was most anxiously awaiting it.

I do not, however, by any means share in your apprehension. I rather believe that if all goes well with us we will ask you to allow us this heretic work for publication, because I myself am a heretic who has not yet turned into a fanatic. Fanatics, people who are able to take their limitations very seriously, I cannot stand. If one only retains one's superiority and knows what one is doing, one can do a few things which are a little out of line. I also like very much the courage which you plan to show. Perhaps my latest small, recently printed article, *Beyond the Pleasure Principle*, will change somewhat the image of my character in your eyes. Also, I do not think I could easily get along without you.

With such encouragement, Groddeck made arrangements to take time away from his practice for a long vacation. He planned to go at the end of the year, when there was little to do at a spa. Before his preparations were completed, he sent a new article to Freud for the *Journal*, and told him with delight that he had just received the first copy of *Der Seelensucher*. The novel was in print at last, and Groddeck declared that the cover was beautiful, the general effect magnificent and dignified. He was in an exalted mood, when everything he had ever wanted seemed at hand. His divorce from Else, delayed for years by the war and the consequent inflation, was about to become final. He was retreating to his beloved forest to write a book on which he had ruminated for years. And Freud approved.

On the last day of December Groddeck wrote:

> I wish I could in some way let you partake of just a small portion of the joy of living which I have received through you, but I can only do as good boys do with their father, determine to do good work and make you proud of me . . . On Monday I will go on vacation for the first time in six years, to the Black Forest to a little house quite removed from all that is human. Only accompanied by my assistant [Emmy] and without any servant, without danger of seeing anybody. She will cook and I will chop wood and sweep the rooms and we will walk about in the forest and feed the deer and the birds, and rest. And if heaven should want it, I will start the book about the unconscious, something popular.

The "little house" was a wooden hut built by a grateful patient. It became the forerunner of a series of retreats, where he could rest and write.

Freud thanked him for the new article, which was "clever and fresh as always." Of the novel, just released to the public, he said of the title character, "Many will be pleased by him, many will be annoyed." Ferenczi sent greetings through Freud. "I envy your forest trip, but why not a different time of year?"

12

THE ID AND THE IT

Winter was the best time of year for a vacation. During warm weather, Baden-Baden was crowded with tourists, and Groddeck worked six days a week, including Sunday. (He still took Monday for his day of rest, and always left the Sanitarium.)

The forest trip was productive. The writing went easily and rapidly. If Freud had expressed doubts about the book, Groddeck would probably have written it anyway but he was not overstating the case when he declared his love for Freud was that of a son who longs to please his father. In conversation he said more than once, "I love Freud just this side of idolatry." It had been Freud's praise of *Der Seelensucher* which kept Groddeck seeking to publish it, and the approval of the projected book made the writing a pleasure. Only one disagreement persisted—the question of the unconscious and the It.

In the early spring of 1921, five chapters of the new book were ready. They were written in the form of letters to a dear friend, an intelligent young woman who wanted to know something about psychoanalysis. The form gave Groddeck freedom to write with an easy frankness which would have been impossible any other way. The second letter answered questions supposedly asked by the friend in response to the first letter, and so it went. He let his imagination take flight; he explained concepts in terms of personal experience, drawing on events from his own life, stories told him by patients, and the experiences of his imaginary correspondent. The first five letters set the tone and pace of the book. He sent the pages to Freud and awaited a response.

On April 17, Freud replied.

> It is Sunday and I will make a holiday of answering your letter. The five letters are charming. I am determined not to let them go to any other publisher. Especially where you speak of yourself they are irresistible. I would like to tell you that my daughter, who aside from me was the only reader, even though not without antipathy acquired from The Hague, has received the same impression.

Though she never fully shared her father's high regard for Groddeck, Anna Freud was most impressed with the new manuscript.

Freud went on to say:

> Well, now, I am very anxious about the continuation, whether you will be able to continue to mold the raw material with such ease and whether you will be able to succeed with all your capriccios to present clearly the piece of ground from which you spring forth. Your style is captivating, your language like music.
>
> And now to speak of more serious matters. I understand well why the unconscious is not enough for you and that you consider the It needed. *I feel just as you do, only I have a special talent for being satisfied with a fragment.** For the unconscious is really only a phenomenon, an indication in the lack of a better acquaintance, such as if I were to say: the gentleman in Havelock whose face I cannot see clearly, what would I do if he should appear once without this piece of clothing.

* Authors' italics.

Therefore, I have long recommended in my intimate circle not to contrast the unconscious and the conscious, but to contrast an interrelated Ego with the repressed splintered off from it. But this still does not solve the difficulty. The Ego is equally deeply unconscious in its depths and still it flows together with the core of the unrepressed. A truer representation therefore seems to be that the links and separations as observed by us only have meaning in the relatively superficial levels and not in the depth, for which your It would be the proper term, maybe thusly:

[*Here he drew a little diagram*]

We will discuss it further when the little book (yours) is ready. I would prefer to discuss it verbally, rather than to write, but how could we do that? Could you get away for a few days during the summer to come to Gastein or wherever I will be later?

You also say that I have removed myself from the erotic. My next small publication will perhaps show you that when I do that I will still take Eros with me on this trip. (*Group Psychology and the Analysis of the Ego.*)

With sincerest regards and in expectation,
Your devoted Freud

Less than six months earlier Freud had been complaining that Groddeck "took our mutual, undefined and easy-running unconscious and gave it all sorts of positive qualities which grew out of a secret source of self-realization." Now he admitted that the "easy-running unconscious was not enough." He, too, needed a broader concept and proposed to take it from Groddeck. The argument, after four years, seemed to have ended.

Actually it was a temporary truce. The full scope of Groddeck's *It* was not appreciated by Freud or any other analyst. One of Groddeck's firm beliefs was, for example, that the little girl is female from the beginning, and that penis envy, while present, is not a powerful force of the It. Groddeck might have expressed his view of the supremacy of the It: "If the It wanted women to have penises, they would have them."

Like many of Freud's followers, Ernest Jones occasionally found it difficult to admit that some of Freud's ideas came to him from others. Freud himself had no such difficulty in acknowledging his indebtedness. The Jones biography of Freud makes little of the source of the new idea. Freud told Ferenczi, Jones writes, that he was occupied in "either a small book or else nothing at all. I will not yet reveal to you the title, only that it has to do with Groddeck."

In explaining the translation in Freud's works of *Das Es* as the *Id*, Jones says that it was decided to use the Latin for consistency. He mentions that the *It* had been extensively employed by Nietzsche and "popularized" by Groddeck. Actually, Freud's book employing the new term came out in the spring of 1923, the same season as Groddeck's *Book of the It*.

Jones explains the change that required the new term:

> The conception of the Id was both more comprehensive and more fruitful than the early one of the Unconscious, which in some respects it tended in practice to replace. It is broader, and the reasons Freud gave for this extension are very instructive. Originally his conception of the unconscious had made it synonymous with what was repressed; indeed it was through his discovery of the latter that he had arrived at his concept of the unconscious. For some time now, however, Freud had been realizing that the unconscious contained more than what was repressed. Apart from the hypothetical question of the state of the primary impulses before the forces of repression had been brought to bear on them, the most convincing reason for surmising the presence of other contents in the unconscious besides the repressed material was a purely clinical experience . . . When a patient manifests the

easily recognized signs of resistance he is in most cases aware of his repugnance and recalcitrancy, but situations occur, and not infrequently, in which he is quite unaware of it; in other words, an unconscious resistance must be operative. The repressed impulses themselves are of course striving to reach consciousness to obtain expression, so that any resistances must emanate from the ego itself. The unavoidable conclusion follows that the ego is not limited to what the subject consciously calls his self, but is contained below the threshold of consciousness; part of the ego is conscious, part unconscious. And the latter part is not merely preconscious; it is unconscious in the fullest sense, since much work is needed to make it conscious.

Groddeck had been saying much the same to Freud since 1917, and Freud had been unable to accept the argument. Even after he accepted it, and gave credit to Groddeck for it, he had some reservations. It became clear, when the two books were translated, that it had been wise to distinguish between the "Id" and the "It," because Freud's concept of the Id, broadened as it was, was still not as broad as Groddeck's concept of the It. Freud's book presented a description of what he meant by the Id, with his indebtedness to Groddeck.

> Now I think we shall gain a great deal by following the suggestion of a writer, who, from personal motives, vainly insists that he has nothing to do with the rigors of pure science. I am speaking of Georg Groddeck, who is never tired of pointing out that the conduct through life of what we call our ego is essentially passive, and that, as he expresses it, we are "lived" by unknown and uncontrollable forces. We have all had impressions of the same kind, even though they may not have overwhelmed us to the exclusion of all others, and we need feel no hesitation in finding a place for Groddeck's in the fabric of science. I propose to take it into account by calling the entity which starts out

from the system Pcpt and begins by being Pcs the ego, and by following Groddeck in giving to the other part of the mind, into which this entity extends and which behaves as though it were Ucs, the name of Id (Es).

It is interesting that Freud, who was bored by struggles for priority in scientific discovery, and wrote many articles on people who had made observations that anticipated his own, should have inspired in so many of his followers a jealous protection of his originality. Possibly Jones was unaware of the exchange of letters about the unconscious and the It, but with the publication of Freud's book, *The Ego and the Id*, it is inexcusable that there should still be psychoanalysts who scarcely recognize the name of Groddeck.

Groddeck himself, after his initial painful disappointment at finding that Freud had anticipated him, never troubled again about priority. He gave Freud the Id as a gift—he, too, had borrowed it, from Nietzsche. It was a tool, more useful for him than any other, but only a tool.

In May, Groddeck wrote to Freud, once again inviting him to visit Baden-Baden. This time he included Anna in the invitation. He was delighted that Freud liked the letters and promised to send more as soon as they were ready. He then went on to describe the successful treatment of a woman with chronic heart disease and chronic kidney infection. The account, given fully in the letter and described many years later before a Psychotherapeutic Congress, is an excellent example of the way Groddeck handled patients at this time.

> The first three weeks of combined physical and mental treatment produced good results, but things came to a stop in the fourth week, and then there was a serious relapse. I therefore decided to take certain action which I had often found beneficial, though only when taken at the right juncture in any treatment. I explained matters to the patient as follows: "You know you have been up and about and have had no pain

these many years, although the condition of the heart has been the same. That you are now ill and have edema cannot therefore be due to the heart trouble, but to some disturbance between the action of the heart and the opposition of your organism to this action. The attempt to strengthen the power of the heart has failed, as you know. The attempt we have made during the first three weeks to diminish the resistance against the heart's action led to improvement, yet during the last eight days, although apparently the treatment has not changed, we have first come to a standstill and then lost ground. That shows, if we understand the message, that something in the treatment has changed so that it no longer is effectual. All treatment included two factors: First, what is prescribed, and second, the personal influence of the doctor. Since no change has been made in the regimen prescribed for you, the disturbance must concern my personal influence. I would ask you to think over what it is that you have against me." I received the usual reply, the patient had nothing at all against me. At last, as I remained obstinate in my belief and the patient equally so, I restored to cunning and asked her, without warning, to repeat one of the commandments. At once, without stopping to think, she repeated the commandment against adultery. 'Why do you think that I have committed adultery?' I asked. "I have been told that you were divorced, and although your first wife is still alive, you have married again." "That is so," I replied, "but you forget that I am a Protestant, and so my faith does not prohibit a second marriage while my first wife is alive. But when did you hear that my first wife was still living?" "Eight days ago." "Then that was when you first began to get worse. I must now tell you something else if we are to get any good from all this. You have made a charge against me which cannot be justified, and this you did knowing that I was a Protestant. Now unjust charges are only made when the accuser has committed the fault with which he taxes another. I know, then, quite certainly, that you yourself have broken your marriage vow."

Greatly moved, my patient then told me the following story: "It is not the vow of earthly fidelity that I have broken, but a far more sacred pledge. As a young girl I longed to be a nun, but my parents set themselves against my desire and I gave it up, making a secret and inviolable oath to myself that I would remain a virgin for the whole of my life. This vow, made to God, I have betrayed, for, as you know, I am married. Since my wedding I have had bitter struggles with my conscience, always renewing them as soon as they die down. I have spoken of it in confession, but although the priest has assured me that no validity can attach to such a vow, and therefore no mortal sin is committed in breaking it, still I never lose my burden of anxiety nor find any peace of mind." After this confession I had a further conversation with the patient, and advised her when she returned home to discuss the situation with a priest, not in confession, but in his private capacity. (What she had told me showed that she did not trust the judgment of the priest as her confessor, and so that could only increase her sense of guilt.) This she promised to do.

After I had gone from the room she started to urinate, and in such quantities as I have hardly ever experienced with any patient, certainly not with any suffering from incapacity to urinate like this patient. Within four hours her weight had gone down by five kilograms, and the next morning by another kilogram. From the moment she told her story her condition grew better every day, and in a short time every sign of defective compensation had disappeared. Some idea of her condition may be gathered from her loss of weight, which amounted to four kilos in the first four weeks of the treatment, and in the weeks following her confession to twenty-five kilos. The patient returned to her home quite recovered.

This case history, like all of Groddeck's case histories, fascinated Freud. He wrote that he could not come to visit, though he wished he could. He longed "to sit on my rear end for a few weeks and watch what kind of artistry you perform, just as I, still earlier, did with Bernheim." He hoped that something unexpected would come up to make the trip possible, in which case he would arrive unannounced.

Groddeck went on hoping for the visit. He sent along more chapters from his book. The work was going smoothly. Indeed, the book seemed to be writing itself. He was so full of ideas that he was sure he would have to cut to make the thing a reasonable size.

"From *Der Seelensucher*," Groddeck wrote, "I hear something every now and then, but the nicest are the experiences which I have with my closest friends. They all hide it very carefully."

Groddeck had no idea at this writing that his novel, which in its format had looked to him so "magnificent and dignified" was causing a sensation, not only among his friends, but in psychoanalytical circles.

Jones said that it was a "racy" book which contained some bawdy passages. Other analysts, particularly Oskar Pfister, the Swiss clergyman, felt that it was not fitting that a scientific publishing house should have published it. Not only did it cause argument, there was a special protest meeting of the Swiss Psychoanalytical Society. Indignant letters poured in from scandalized analysts to Freud, who said amiably in a letter to Pfister, "I am defending Groddeck energetically against your respectability. What would you have said had you been a contemporary of Rabelais?"

When news of the excitement finally reached Groddeck, he found it amusing. When the shouting had died away, the first edition was sold out and the book went into a second printing. Groddeck thought of writing a sequel, and Freud was not averse to the plan.

The book of Letters was progressing. Another batch of manuscript went to Freud, who answered from his vacation spot at Bad Gastein. He praised the new section of the book, but was beginning to feel uneasy about the reactions of others. Perhaps in the light of the violent reactions to *Der Seelensucher*, it might be well if Groddeck "could sacrifice a few little improprieties and you could change a few details to which different analysts might take exception . . . The fragments of the analyses of patients cry for more." He said that he planned to go on to Seefeld for the remainder of his holiday, and would have no time for a visit to Baden-Baden.

Groddeck, disappointed again, tried to explain himself:

> May I give a word of explanation about my lack of inhibition. At the time of my apprenticeship, words, exact and objective words, played a very great role. I myself could never stand to be as exact and objective as was asked, and because I couldn't do it, I have, wherever it interested me, namely in medicine, closely observed those who have claimed fame in this peculiarity. Because I have wanted to see their faults, I have seen them, and I have thus come to the peculiar over-evaluation of the subjective and debatable. From this has then developed a form of exactitude of the paradox which might very much appear unrestrained, and which, in a certain sense, it is. Definition has suffered most from this . . . Little by little, then, I lost the understanding of definition, so that I had great difficulty understanding your meaning and many times I can't even do it. There arose a barrier which has closed off a good part of the world for me. The most important part of my inability to limit myself is not that I go off into endless distances but that I don't wish to keep order in that which is limited . . . In other words, I do not see the boundaries between things, only their run-

ning into one another. That is a mistake, but also it has its great advantages. Systematic heads need for their value people of my kind. Sometimes a little pepper is not to be looked down upon. In the final analysis, my lack of inhibition has probably been determined through my parents and brothers and sister. We were brought up with an arrogant sentence which said, There are good people, there are bad people, and there are Groddecks. Between us and others there is, therefore, a barrier . . . It must have meant very much for me that I remained the sole member of my family. My becoming poor and healthy with some thinking can be dated after the deaths in my family . . .

Forgive the long-winded exposition. Be kind to me and have faith. I will work the letters over to clean up, if possible, that which causes objections. There will probably still be enough left to give me the gratification of this one or that one speaking out his anathema about me.

In a few days I will send you another batch of Girl-friend letters. To your question as to composition, volume, and final objective, I can only answer conditionally. There is no composition in it; the final aim was to write a universally understandable book about psychoanalysis which would facilitate treatment. Meanwhile, I have discovered that books are of no use to treatment. Therefore, I write without a final objective in mind, only for my own pleasure and the pleasure of those who like my way of writing, to dispel their boredom, and to pull them closer to me. Perhaps you will tell me when it is enough.

I really don't want to read over what I have just written to you. It is miserably hot and even though I sit in almost complete nudity I am dripping with wisdom and sweat. I would prefer it if you were here . . .

The persistent attitude of humility seems almost out of character in the man who fought Freud for four years on the meaning of the It. He offers to cut his book to a length to suit Freud; he agrees to tone down passages which might offend other psychoanalysts; he promises to delete and rewrite.

Actually it is not out of character. Groddeck argued in defense of the It because he needed it in his work. Without the It, he could not explain himself. In the disagreement about Ibsen he did not concede, merely remarking that "you certainly think as you did before." But now he was writing about psychoanalysis, and, in his relation to Freud, felt himself to be truly the humble student, the docile pupil, eager to please the master. From Seefeld, where he was spending part of his vacation, Freud wrote that the third installment of the letters had arrived. "They are equally as fascinating as the former ones, perhaps not quite as daring."

Of course they were not quite as daring. Freud had considered the earlier ones too daring. Now that they were toned down to please him, he rather regretted the loss. However, the whole thing impressed him and he wanted it to "come among people whose prejudices and limitations it should loosen up and inspire them to expressions of outrage."

Though he could not visit Baden-Baden himself, he said he would be sending a replacement.

13

THE BOOK OF THE IT

The replacement was Sandor Ferenczi. This warm, tender-hearted, lovable man had been ill for long periods of his life. He married late, partly because his health was so precarious. Jones considered him a hypochondriac, but he was not entirely fair. For one thing, Ferenczi always stood in a special relationship to Freud, who looked on him almost as a son. Whatever their disagreements, Freud was always pleased when they could be on good terms again. Even Georg Grod-deck, to Jones never more than "an amusing oddity," had a special relationship to Freud. In spite of his dozens of inestimable services, Jones was never a favorite son, and it must have been hard for him to understand Freud's fondness for somewhat eccentric people.

In 1921, Ferenczi was suffering from nephrosclerosis complicated by severe headaches, and Felix Deutsch, who was Freud's physician, was consulted. Deutsch sent the patient to Groddeck.

Ferenczi came to Baden-Baden with his wife, Gisela. The men developed a friendship which was to last all their lives, and their wives became close friends. After a short stay Ferenczi returned home "greatly refreshed," free of symptoms and optimistic about his future health. From that time on he took regular "therapeutic holidays" in Baden-Baden.

There is no record of what treatment he received. With other sufferers from kidney disease, Groddeck often combined psychotherapy with massage; sometimes he advised the baths. After 1909, there was sometimes no physical treatment at all. He treated the patient, not the disease, and kidney disease was not the same in all patients. Whatever Groddeck did at the time, Ferenczi was able to return to work, despite a permanently damaged kidney, for many years.

After the Ferenczis left, Groddeck returned to his book. In December he wrote to Freud to say that the book was finished and he was working over the letters. He could have gone on, but he did not want the book to be too long. In the rewriting, he promised, "I shall try to take out all hostility and to make them especially readable."

They had lost something for him. In the beginning, when he had allowed himself to write exactly as he pleased, he had liked them. They had seemed to write themselves. But he had pruned and tamed them, and now, though "I still like a few of them . . . on the whole the entire thing has become too ironical for me. The lectures from which they arose had enthusiasm and that seems to have crawled a little behind the laughing mask."

The loss of enthusiasm was the price Groddeck paid for Freud's approval. The letters were no longer entirely his own, but partly Freud's. The price was not too high for him, but having paid it, he wanted approval as his due.

He went on, in a letter, with other things.

> Meanwhile Ferenczi has been here. I had great pleasure from him . . . He promised to come again and I think he will keep his promise . . . thus far I have been satisfied with the replacement, but it is still only a replacement and it does not deliver me from the promise to pester you constantly until you, yourself, will come.

Baden-Baden is worth seeing and neither Troll* nor I
have missed pumping both Ferenczis as to the wishes
and needs of Freud. You will not believe what a role
this much-dreamt-of fantasy plays in my life.

I will send you the manuscript of the letters when
they are ready to be printed toward the end of the
month. They can start printing at any time now. During January and February I plan to go into a loneliness
and I will then start the second part of *Der Seelensucher*. That will probably keep me busy for the entire
next year. I was very pleased with Ferenczi's criticism.
He brought it with him when he came to Baden-
Baden . . .

My practical activity is still full of surprises and I
hope to be more successful the more freshly I attempt
it. The danger of philosophizing and of occultism are
thus far not here for me. For the former I have an
inclination, but the occult is taboo for me.

I am engaged in the treatment of a lady with arthritis
deformans in both knee joints and habitual patellar
luxation. I hope it will be a success. Until now the
main result is that I fell off my bicycle on my way to
the patient and have shattered my right knee. This has
once more led to self-analysis and the result is excellent.

Ferenczi wrote that Baden-Baden might be a possibility for the Congress of 1923. I would be tickled to
death if it were so, and I really don't believe that one
could find a better or more convenient spot.

Ferenczi's review of *Der Seelensucher*, which appeared
later in *Imago*, must have delighted Groddeck after all the
shouting against the book. Best of all, it was written objectively, before Ferenczi became his patient and friend. It was a
sympathetic appraisal from within official circles, only the

* Emmy. In the book of Letters, the signature is Patrik Troll.

second in Groddeck's experience, and both written by Ferenczi.

The introduction to the review was a description of Groddeck's work in the analytic treatment of organic disease, included for the benefit of those who were unfamiliar with his writings. Ferenczi then went on to speak of the novel.

> I am no literary critic and do not presume to judge the aesthetic value of this novel; I believe, however, that it cannot be a bad book which succeeds, as this does, in holding the reader from beginning to end and in putting difficult biological and physiological problems in a humorous and even comic form, and in presenting with gentle humor crudely grotesque and deeply tragic scenes which, taken by themselves, would have been repugnant.
>
> He wittily represents his hero, Muller-Weltlein, the "Seelensucher," as a genial fool, and the reader can never be certain when he is revealing the results of his genius or of his folly. In this way Groddeck-Weltlein is able to ventilate many things which he could not either in a scientific book or in a seriously meant fantasy without challenging the whole world. The indignant bourgeois would immediately call for the strait jacket; but as the mocking author has already donned it himself, even the guardians of public morals have no choice but to put a good face on it and laugh. Moreover, many a physician, thinker, and philosopher will find in this book the beginnings of a philosophy free from the shackles of traditional mysticism and dogmatism and the rudiments of a re-evaluation of man and institutions. The educational value of the book lies in the fact that the author, like Swift, Rabelais, and Balzac in the past, has torn the mask from the face of the pious, hypocritical spirit of the age and has exposed the cruelty and lust hidden behind it while at the same time comprehending its inevitability . . .

For this review alone, Groddeck would have felt forever grateful to Ferenczi.

At the end of the year Freud wrote wishing Groddeck "all good and happy things for the coming year of 1922." It was very pleasant, said Freud, to know that at any time he felt himself failing there was an asylum for him in Baden-Baden, but the prospect of a visit was poor. He was working hard, seeing nine students daily, but only one patient. He was writing nothing, but spending a lot of time reading the manuscripts of others. He promised that when Groddeck's manuscript arrived he would drop everything else in order to facilitate publication. It was good news that *Der Seelensucher* was to have a second part.

As happened now and then in their correspondence, Groddeck's letter, dated the 30th, crossed Freud's of the 29th. Groddeck wrote that he was sending the completed manuscript of *The Book of the It* and asked Freud to pass it along to Rank, who was editor of the *Verlag*. He offered three possible titles, from which Freud was to choose the one he liked best. He was preparing to go to the mountains for two months and gave Freud the address.

The book was now so much Freud's that he even left it to Freud to choose a title. It seems a pity that the original manuscript is not available. It would be interesting to see how much change took place in the effort "to take out all hostility" and to make the book more acceptable to analysts.

"Of that which is happening among the psychoanalysts I hear very little," Groddeck wrote. "I live too far from Berlin. Every now and then Ferenczi notifies me of something. Otherwise I live from the journals and from my own experiences."

Emmy had the plan of translating Freud's work into Swedish, and Groddeck understood enough Swedish to help her. He mentioned this to Freud, again referring to Emmy as *Troll*, the name with which he signed the letters in *The Book of the It*.

> My practice this year has given me some very good results, for my own development, also. If it continues this way for a few more years you will yet have pleasure from your most fanciful and most faithful student.
>
> It is warm and it is fun to live here, almost as though it were spring already. We are in the midst of preparations for our departure; we are packing cans, blankets, dishes, and smoking utensils, which I would hate to lack. The boots all have nails, and the stomach, which has become rather large, is longing to lose some of its fat.* Habbakuk, the cat, and Fick, the canary bird, will be taken along. Troll-Voigt has packed the cookbook and my mouth is watering with her description of the Swedish art of cookery.
>
> And why do I write you all this? So that you might want to make a trip to us and with us; if you won't do it soon, I can at least imagine that you are joining me in your thoughts.
>
> And now, finally, best wishes for the new year. All good things for you and yours.

The vacation was not at first successful. For a month, he could not write. He was exceedingly tired, with a need for long hours of sleep, a symptom he had not experienced since his school days. Freud was silent and Groddeck began to worry. At last he wrote to Freud.

> After a few forced marches through the snow in the mountains I am once more cheerful . . . I consider your silence about the Girlfriend letters as a sign that you

---

* An allusion to pregnancy; when he was preparing to write something, his abdomen enlarged.

have found a few objectionable items, yes, that even a few important points do not suit you. As sorry as I would be about that, it would not be irreparable. The arrangement of the letter form permits all sorts of changes. That was the main reason that I chose such an outlandish form of writing. I count on your criticisms and will use them . . . Personally I don't mind if I make mistakes in my works. It would only be unpleasant for you if you were annoyed . . .

Few sons are so devoted that their productions are of value only as they give pleasure to the father. Groddeck's worry was not that he might have to re-shape his book, but that it might cause displeasure to Freud. This attitude was not fostered by Freud, who made suggestions in a friendly way and never insisted on a change. It was Groddeck's doing. He put himself in the position of the youngest son who must please the father at any cost. The book was already so changed that he no longer recognized it as his own, and he was prepared to make further changes, anything at all that Freud wanted.

Freud replied with an apology for the delay in writing. He had been occupied with correspondence, profession and business, and Ferenczi and Abraham had been guests in the house. For weeks he had been ill with a debilitating influenza. His silence did not mean that the manuscript displeased him.

"On the contrary, it would have been all right with me to present you to a worshipping, feeble-minded public with all your misbehavior and your originality and to ask that you be taken just as you are." But Rank, as the *Verlag* editor, had a few suggestions, and Rank's judgment was good.

The letter went on with a frank and friendly statement of Freud's attitude.

My critical deviations from you appeared in the beginning of our correspondence. That I do not share your Panpsychism, which amounts almost to mysticism, but

rather admit my agnosticism much earlier; that I believe you too-early despised reason and science . . . all
this I have recognized as your good personal right and
it has neither disturbed me in the enjoyment of your
writings, nor confused me in the estimation of your
original finds and interpretations.

The letter did not comfort Groddeck. He wanted more,
he wanted some kind of official endorsement, or perhaps the
sort of warm praise an affectionate father might give to a
gifted son. Whatever it was he wanted, he did not find it in
this letter, and a week later he sent Freud a long reply. He
had had a message from Rank, recommending cuts in the
manuscript. He had agreed to all of Rank's suggestions. He
would make any changes Rank wished, because of what
Freud had said about Rank's good judgment.

Thus far everything is going along satisfactorily, but I
have taken this opportunity to ask Rank how the publishing house is disposed toward my works, and I
would like to pose the same question to you personally.
What still concerns me is that I, a pronounced sub-
jectivist, am right in the midst of those who believe
objectively, still shackled with the chronic realization
of not knowing anything. Strangely enough, what has
made me brave enough to come out into the open was
your personal approval of my works. Now I do not
have the conviction that this approval extends also to
the Letters and I would like to ask you to please tell
me whether I have become troublesome. It is not prob-
able that once I have started upon a path I could stand
still on it or even divert from it. In the Letters, there is,
odd as they may seem, the clearly apparent direction in
which I am going. If this direction, which leads more
and more into the dark, goes along with the work of
your students, it would be most to my liking. I know of
no one else but you to whom I could turn with this
important question, whether the leaders of the psycho-

analytical movement will approve or at least endure that which I have written or will write in the same vein. Please be kind enough to write to me.

Freud, who had already praised the Letters on half a dozen occasions, showed neither surprise nor impatience at this fresh demand for approval. He did not even indicate that he might be growing tired of Groddeck's frequent requests for reassurance. His letter was kind and fatherly.

> I am sorry if we have confused you momentarily. Fishing for compliments*—that doesn't seem quite like you. Please don't be unhappy. Others like to fall away from me. When I am with someone it is for a long time. I have enjoyed the Letters to the friend very much . . .

He sent along a gift copy of a new edition of his lectures. Groddeck was content. He wrote a pleasant letter to say that the pretty volume gave him great pleasure. His vacation was coming to an end; he had done no work, but he had enjoyed the rest.

There were several letters that year, but no further complaints or questions. The "Girlfriend Letters" were finally given the title *Das Buch vom Es* (*The Book of the It*), either by Freud or by Rank.

In May, Groddeck sent an article for the *Journal*, and in the summer Ferenczi made a visit to Baden-Baden, combining therapy with a vacation. Ferenczi never tired of singing Groddeck's praises, and spoke so often of the beneficial effects of an "analytical holiday" that several others tried it. Sanitarium Groddeck often had more analysts than laymen during the warm weather.

Groddeck very much enjoyed Ferenczi's visits. He said of this visit, in a letter to Freud, "It refreshed my soul to see

---

* Written in English.

Ferenczi. I feel so close to him in his way of being and we have become good friends."

On this occasion, for the first time, Ferenczi brought to Baden-Baden those of his analysands who wanted to continue their analyses uninterrupted. They took rooms in the town and had their regular sessions with Ferenczi, who in turn had his regular sessions with Groddeck. It was a satisfactory arrangement for everyone concerned and Ferenczi continued the practice for many years.

In September, the International Psychoanalytical Congress was held in Berlin. Groddeck spoke on *The Flight into Philosophy*. This time he had prepared his remarks in advance, and the speech was well organized. An abstract of the talk was published in the *International Journal*. It began:

> The speaker discussed the question whether the present conception of the unconscious suffices for purposes of psychoanalytic treatment. In his opinion there are in the human being forces which are not adequately covered by the term "unconscious," as hitherto used. He proposed to designate these forces, as yet undefined, by the word *Es* (It). He believes all the manifestations of life in man—his outward form, his structure, the alterations and functioning of his organs, his actions and his thoughts, his psychic and physical diseases . . . to be merely different phenomena in which the *Es* is manifested.

The talk was better received than the unfortunate attempt at The Hague. Though many felt he claimed too much for psychoanalysis, still the premise was exciting. At a dinner party given by Eitington, Groddeck and Emmy were made to feel welcome. Lou Salomé was especially friendly and Freud was gracious and charming.

About this congress, Groddeck made no complaints to Freud. He now had a few friends in the society. Ferenczi was his staunch supporter, Karen Horney regarded him with affection and respect, Ernst Simmel planned a visit to Baden-Baden. True, his ideas were received with more understanding by some of the laborers he addressed in his cooperative society, but he no longer expected much from psychoanalysts. He considered them humans with more than their share of human weaknesses.

14

THE EGO AND THE ID

At Christmas, Freud wrote to tell Groddeck of his own latest work. The little book, *Das Ich und das Es* (*The Ego and the Id*) was scheduled for publication, but the publishing house was in a bad way following the crash of the currency. Groddeck's book was scheduled ahead of Freud's, but both were being delayed. About his own book, Freud said, "You remember how early I took the *Es* from you. It was long before I met you, in one of my first letters to you (April 17, 1921) in which I enclosed a drawing which I will change a little in the near future and which will be brought before the public." He explained about the plight of the *Verlag*, but promised to speak to Rank about hurrying things with *Das Buch vom Es*.

In March, 1923, the long-awaited publication took place, and Freud wrote to congratulate Groddeck on its appearance. Once again, he said that he liked it.

> I am very fond of the little book. I consider it meritorious to push people's noses into these fundamentals of analysis from which they have removed themselves from time to time. Besides, the book represents the theoretically significant viewpoint which I have incorporated into my about-to-be-published *Ich und Es*.
>
> In the public this will naturally create more antipathy

and indignation than the charming *Seelensucher*, which could compensate as an artistic elaboration of the undesirable.

Freud had apparently forgotten the reception of the "charming *Seelensucher*." He had had to defend it, not from the general public, but from the analysts themselves. Its raciness was too much for the decorum of the society members.

Groddeck was dissatisfied with Freud's reaction to his book. He did not like its being called "the little book." Perhaps one of his analyst-patients told him that Freud was really not enthusiastic about the work. In any case, in spite of all the praise Freud had given the manuscript, Groddeck became convinced that he did not like the book. Perhaps he expected and hoped that he would make a public announcement of his approval. Freud did voice his favorable opinion occasionally. He told Oskar Pfister, "Groddeck is surely 4/5 right with his relating of organic suffering to the It, and perhaps even with the other 1/5 he points to the right thing."

This remark was not repeated to Groddeck—indeed, Pfister did not publish it until more than twenty years after Groddeck's death, though Freud said it in 1923, immediately after the book came out. Groddeck did not hear of this, but he did hear a statement, "*It* mythology carries me nowhere," supposedly spoken by Freud. One wonders by whom this tidbit was relayed.

In May, as soon as Freud's book was out, he mailed a copy to Groddeck. Groddeck sat down at once to write a letter that was almost as long as the small book it discussed.

Many thanks for sending *das Ich und das Es*. Now I, as godfather, the namegiver, should have a word to say about it, but the only thing I can think of is a comparison which illuminates our interrelationship and our relationship to the world, but which says nothing about the book. In this comparison I appear to myself as a plow, and you the farmer who will use this or perhaps any other plow for his means . . . In one thing we agree, and that is to loosen up the earth, but you wish to sow and, perhaps, God and weather permitting, to reap, but the plow only wants to loosen the ground and avoid rocks which could dull the blade. Because the plow has no eyes but fears the rocks, it balks at times to make the farmer who guides it more cognizant of his pushing, so that it will not become worn out. For the plow it is a matter of life. For the farmer, in the last analysis, it is a matter of money, because he would have to replace the unusable plow with a new one. And besides it is unpleasant for the farmer when his tool becomes useless . . . You yourself can look over the entire field, but I have only a dull sensation of the fact that there is rocky ground. For example, your separation of sadism from the destructive drives. I cling to this and do not wish to go further . . . But I may be wrong, and yet I believe that your effect upon the ground, that is, upon your students, is to know your reaction better than the farmer. Naturally, for you a lack of harvest on this or the other spot is not so important. Today's generation of disciples is only of great importance to us, not to you.

But then comes the truly great boulder, or at least something which I consider such a rock—the physical, where the farmer knows, here is rocky ground. He guides the plow with a careful hand and the plow can feel the careful hand which guides it. It also notices that the farmer keeps his eyes on the fruitful earth of the Es which lies next to it, but it does not understand why the farmer wants to plow the very rocky ground which seems to be of so little value to the plow; the plow only reluctantly goes along to the field of the Ego upon which the separation between psychic and physical is strongly accentuated. And the sentence: "on this Ego hangs consciousness. It dominates accesses to motility, to the removal of energy to the outer world," brings to the plow a real blow. The plow, which has finally begun to realize among its bitter experiences that it is not an Ego, has the tendency to consider the concept of the Ego as a dazzling of the Es. At least it cannot decide to renounce the supposition that each cell has its own consciousness and has therefore also an independent removal. The Ego seems to it to possess not even the motility of a voluntary muscle, much less intestine, kidney, heart, or brain. With this he naturally disowns neither Ego nor Super-Ego. They are for him but tools, not existences. I have the impression that the farmer, for some reason will remain, at least meanwhile, on the field of the so-called psychical, and perhaps he will make quite a few plows unusable without achieving any great harvest. In other words, the plow considers the farmer a little stubborn. But then again it has only the understanding of a plow.

Well, it seems I have become talkative. No offense meant! Like a brightly shining light came the explanation to me of the unconscious guilt from the Oedipus complex and identification. In the father-question I am mindful of some complexes of my own, but meanwhile I cannot deny that I would rather work with the mother than with the father. Perhaps that will improve when my homosexuality becomes freer. The castration investigation can hardly be by-passed by nursing and weaning and meanwhile I believe that this fear applies to the mother as well as to the father and that in the emptying out there will be found a third root, splintering from the semen and the egg and—what may be related to your destructive drives—expulsion of material, what the cells' Es does not wish to use.

And finally (I could talk on much more, but the main point is given to you in this comparison, which proves that I am by nature un-understandable, a tool) —and finally there is a secret laughter about movable energy, libido, which works in the service of the pleasure principle to overcome blocking and to facilitate displacement and to which it is inconsequential to a certain degree in what manner this displacement happens. And we could leave aside the eternally unanswered questions to which it belongs since we do have the instrument of this movable energy and only at the most lend it sometimes to other beings which can make this instrument movable.

> Most cordially,
> Your fearful Groddeck

The bitterness and despair Groddeck felt at Freud's use of his *Es*-concept are clearly evidenced in this letter. Here, for the first time, he shows that he is aware that Freud has declined to accept the position of father. "Today's generation of your disciples is only of great importance to us, not to you."

Like the son who wants endless approval for his productions, he expresses frustration that his father is not adequately impressed and is really only concerned with his own work. Groddeck was correct in his belief that Freud at this time could not accept his unified picture of the human dynamism.

The over-long, tendentious analogy to the blind plow and the far-seeing farmer can be explained by Groddeck's fear of open expression of anger toward Freud. That he should use this analogy, particularly when we know he was fond of considering the earth as Mother Earth, suggests how much he wanted to be thought the effective tool of Freud.

He was now convinced that Freud did not so regard him.

In official circles *The Book of the It* was much better received than the novel had been. For one thing, Freud had influenced Groddeck to tone it down and it did not offend. For another, the style was easy and informal, and the intelligent layman, for whom, after all, it was intended, could understand it without having to consult a technical dictionary. There was a marked scarcity of technical terms, but no over-simplification.

Karen Horney, who had maintained sporadic correspondence with Groddeck after meeting him at the Berlin Congress, wrote a long letter. She had taken the book with her on vacation.

Your train of thought was brought close to me through two occurrences: the death of my brother which in the beginning I considered as something totally senseless— he belonged to those people who seem to burst with the joy of living—and in the face of this after many weeks I arrived at the conclusion: something in him had wanted to die. The admission I tend to accept generally and about it I have only one misgiving, and that is that it is too much of what we want to believe. It seems to me on the whole that you smuggle omnipotence back into the Es. But the good thing is exactly this, that you had the courage to make something out of your fantasies of omnipotence. And with this I arrive at the point which has pleased me most in your book, and that is the grandiose candor (Dr. Abraham would say that this is really only exhibitionism) with which you include yourself among this whole confusion . . . That is splendid. If you had enjoyed the questionable good fortune of living within an analytical circle, then you might understand this awareness better. Because here we are no less hypocritical than the norm, only a little different. Above all, it appears repeatedly as a silent presupposition that the "neurotic" has all these embarrassing complexes. It is like the pious Christians and their "We are all sinners" which can become very uncomfortable if you point out to them some concrete examples of such sins . . .

Others admired the book. Ferenczi and Simmel praised it extravagantly. Freud, who had already said he was fond of the book, wrote in June and praised it again. The letter was short, explaining that he had been ill "and had an operation in my mouth,* and now I have lost a dear grandchild after three weeks' suffering from miliary tuberculosis. This is painful and makes one silent."

---

* The first operation for cancer.

15

OF CHILDBIRTH,
EYESIGHT, AND NUMBERS

Groddeck had long held some pet theories about pregnancy
and childbirth, and during the summer he had the opportunity
of testing them.

On November 8, 1923, he wrote Freud:

> It has been a long time since you heard from me, but I
> have thought of you all the more often. Basically the
> thought of Freud never leaves me at all.
>
> Despite all the strange happenings in Germany we
> continue to live our old lives. The work proceeds along
> its course, sometimes with, sometimes without success.
> Twice in the course of the summer I have had the
> opportunity to observe in my sanitarium pregnancy,
> delivery, and the first weeks of life in the infant. The
> supposition that especially good results with psycho-
> analysis could be achieved in the field of obstetrics has
> reinforced itself with this. The difficulties of pregnancy
> —both were primiparas, one was 33 years old—disap-
> peared very rapidly. The deliveries were short and
> easy; even the older one exclaimed at the expulsion of
> the head through the vagina, "Ah, how beautiful, how
> beautiful!"

It was not until the '40's that Grantly Read's "natural" childbirth was given wide publicity. In writing of Read's technique Erik Erikson called it:

> . . . one of the most encouraging experiences of my professional life. The facts are by now well known, although the necessary data for a final evaluation may not yet be available. In the terms used here, we would say that the objective is childbirth without anxiety. The expectant mother will feel some fear because she knows that pain is inevitable. But the fact that the mother has learned, by exercise and instructions, to be aware of the location and the function of the contractions which cause the pain; and the fact that she expects, at the height of the curve of pain, to have the privilege of choosing consciously whether or not she wishes to receive relief by drugs: this entirely judicious situation keeps her from developing the state of anxiety which in the past was caused by ignorance and superstition and which, more often than not, was the real cause of excessive pain.

When Frieda Fromm-Reichmann heard of the great interest in Read's "new" technique, she was amused. "Groddeck was saying this 40 years ago," she said.

The increasing interest in using psychotherapy in obstetrical situations—even the present interest in hypnosis—was clearly anticipated by Groddeck. Unfortunately, his plan for a maternity section in his sanitarium never materialized.

The letter to Freud continued:

> The course of the confinement has touched me very strangely. The customary antipathy of women to nursing the child could be followed up to its roots and could be eliminated. With one, whose milk suddenly stopped for 24 hours, the secretion of milk began again after an old and carefully suppressed hostility against her own mother become apparent.

The Wild Analyst / 136

Nowhere in his writings or in his letters did Groddeck make mention of the reasons for his own mother's inability to nurse any but her first child. This is the sort of oversight which makes a reader wonder. He was able to see his father's unhappiness in the relationship to the mother, and the strange behavior of the mother at her daughter's confirmation, but when he was investigating mother-child relationships he never spoke of his own mother. Perhaps he was afraid to look into his own mother relationship too closely; certainly this was not a conscious fear.

He did concern himself with problems of nursing, and wrote about it later in an article, but here he said, "I could give evidence for the view that disturbance of the milk and breast inflammation in recently delivered mothers are especially open to successful psychotherapeutic treatment," and went on to other symptoms of the disturbance in the mother-child relationship.

> But especially it became clear to me that there are a number of infant difficulties which are caused either consciously or unconsciously by the mother and which disappear after the analysis of the mother.* Everything was so instructive that the wish awakened in me to have more technical skill in the field of delivery. I would then without further ado connect a maternity home with my sanitarium. There is still much to learn in the field of the study of the soul of mother and child, as well as for the practice of obstetrics.
>
> There are a few other things which I have seen which lie in my own direction. Unfortunately, the more one is active, the confident self-deception about one's own discoveries becomes less and less, and it becomes increasingly difficult not to lose one's direction among the multitude of ways in the labyrinth of the uncon-

* This means, some talks with the mother, not, of course, a classical psychoanalysis.

scious. There is hardly anything else to report. I spend more and more time watching carefully.

In the middle of December I plan to close the sanitarium. We—Emmy and I, who, by the way, have finally been married in a civil ceremony—will then go to Holland, Denmark, and Sweden, where I shall give lectures. However, nothing has been definitely settled.

From time to time I receive news of your welfare. I have also received the news of your operations. My thoughts and good wishes are with you whom I love so dearly.

Freud immediately sent congratulations on the marriage. "Basically I am still for respectability," he said. Possibly the presence of Frau Von Voigt at congresses had contributed to the general disapproval of Groddeck. He never attempted to explain that he had been waiting for years to divorce Else, that war and inflation made an earlier divorce impossible. At any rate, Freud asked for reassurance that marriage would not prevent Emmy from continuing to translate his works into Swedish, and went on to say:

That which you write scientifically is as always interesting, new and hopeful. However, I gladly withdraw myself from all attempts to influence you, which you can't always take too well.

About myself, the only thing to say is that I am ill. You seem to be familiar with the details. Naturally I know that it is the beginning of the end. Whether this will continue directly or with interruptions, one cannot know beforehand, but there must be an end and one will not miss the continuation.

By this time(November 25, 1923), the diagnosis of cancer was known to Freud and to Groddeck. Groddeck was not alarmed. His work had proved to him over and over that a diagnosis was only a title, a definition, and that "cancer" or "heart disease" told nothing. Every cancer was different from every other and would take its individual course.

A few weeks later Emmy wrote to Freud to say that she was continuing with her translations and to invite him to visit Baden-Baden. Freud thanked her for the invitation, but said he was not able to travel. If, in the spring, he felt well again, he would have to work, but he hoped to see the Groddecks at Eastertime at the congress at Salzburg. Emmy had also asked permission to inquire about the Nobel prize for Freud but he told her gently that his name had been suggested many times and turned down as many times.

In 1919, Dr. Millais Culpin, one of England's first psychoanalysts, had called on his friend Dr. William Inman for help in a statistical study. Inman was an ophthalmic surgeon, and from him Culpin wished to learn whether patients suffering visual difficulties had ever been afraid of the dark. Culpin wanted to know what proportion of the general population (Inman's patients) had a fear of the dark as compared with people who were "neurotic" (and sought the aid of a psychiatrist). Culpin guessed that fear of the dark would be an almost universal experience.

Dr. Inman's investigation was soon abandoned. He discovered, as he reported in an article, "Emotion and Eye Symptoms," that "the patients of an ophthalmic surgeon could not be accepted as normal . . . many were of the neurotic type . . . inclined to suffer from phobias . . ." Indeed, it seemed to Inman, as he listened to his patients, that he never saw a "healthy" individual. "Nearly every person," he wrote, "who complained of the effect of glare or bright light, whether natural or artificial, had either definite fear of the dark, or could remember his struggles to get rid of the fear when a child."

Inman's article, written in 1921, was the first of many, most of them presented before the Medical Section of the

British Psychological Society. The first article was reprinted more than 30 years later, unaltered, in the book *Modern Trends in Psychosomatic Medicine,* and even at that late date, in 1955, when the book was released in the United States, many ophthalmologists found Inman's theories startling. If, as Inman claimed, the majority of patients who consult an ophthalmologist are emotionally disturbed, then something must be wrong with the way eye doctors practice. There is scarcely any eye symptom except obvious hysteria which is treated as though it were anything but a mechanical defect.

In 1954, in an addendum to his early paper, Inman said that the views he expressed in 1921 "fell on deaf ears, and the craze for glasses went on undiscouraged."

> But research also went on, and since the few analysts of that time already had enough to do in mental exploration, I determined to be trained myself. Freud directed me to Sandor Ferenczi, a fortunate choice as it happened because a few years earlier the latter himself, apparently incurably ill from kidney disease, had gone for treatment to that master of psychosomatic medicine, Georg Groddeck, and had been cured.

During his analysis with Ferenczi, Dr. Inman, not wishing to interrupt during the summer, went to Baden-Baden when Ferenczi was there, took a room in a hotel, and had his daily hour. One day when Inman had been indulging on the couch in highly speculative theories about disease and the emotions, Ferenczi exclaimed, "Dear me, this is out-Groddecking Groddeck!" But he would only say of Groddeck, when Inman asked who he was, that they must meet one day.

It was Ferenczi, Inman recalled, who warned him that the eye specialists would be the last to accept modern psychological trends. "The eye is such a pure organ!" Ferenczi said.

It is striking that almost no other ophthalmologist has published anything showing an interest in the psychodynamics of the field. In fact, no other group of medical specialists manifests as much resistance to psychoanalytic concepts, if we except psychiatrists.

Yet, if we examine what the eye means, perhaps it is not so surprising. In all languages, seeing is equated with knowing, understanding—often the words are interchangeable.

It is an axiom of medicine that the choice of specialty is dictated by the physician's own interest, and that it is not always a conscious interest. Thus, some of the eminent men in chest diseases are those who have themselves recovered from tuberculosis or have seen the disease in those near to them. The obstetrician admittedly feels that he—not the mother—delivers the baby. It would be of interest to speculate as to what dictates the choice of ophthalmology. Focusing on the problems of others is a well known form of resistance manifested by people undergoing psychoanalysis. Usually it is precisely the problem that they do not wish to see in themselves.

Intense focus on the organ of seeing and the mechanisms of seeing may be viewed as a resistance against awareness of "seeing" (understanding). As a displacement, such as occurs in the transferring of hunger for love to hunger for food in over-eating, it is a common human practice. The displaced focus is then projected by the ophthalmologist onto the patient, to constitute a further line of defense for the ophthalmologist against "insight."

The value of eyeglasses as a shield against too close contact with others has been reported by patients in analysis—even when the lenses make no optical correction. The use of tinted glasses as a disguising device behind which to hide is generally known even to the layman. "Shades," they are often called, and various other names synonymous with hiding.

In January, 1924, Groddeck wrote Freud that Emmy had completed the Swedish translation of *The Psychopathology of*

Everyday Life and it was ready for printing. Emmy had left it in Sweden and was planning to begin immediately on the translation of Freud's lectures.

Groddeck hoped to meet Freud at the congress in the spring. He planned a lecture on the future development of psychoanalysis, "for which this time I shall prepare myself because it will deal with basic questions." He preferred to speak extemporaneously, but he knew that he would face an audience prepared to belittle anything he said, and the topic needed preparation.

Groddeck's letter dealt with a long article of Freud's analyzing an error in numbers which Emmy had been translating. He wrote that, while translating the passage quoted, Emmy had made a discovery which Freud might find valuable, if he had not already thought of it himself. "The communications of an impartial person are always valuable. It deals with the figures 2, 4, 6, 7. Owing to the fact that you have given this example of a number, my wife concludes that all that is connected with it has a special meaning in your unconscious . . . she knows that you were 67 in this year . . . I share her opinion that with this can be found an interrelationship to the deep levels of your unconscious."

The point Emmy and Groddeck wished to make was that Freud apparently expected to die at the age of 67. But having made the observation, Groddeck's letter ended with a long postscript. After he finished writing, he said, he discovered that he had also made an error. He had written 2, 4, 6, 7 as 4, 2, 6, 7. Not to be outdone by Freud, he went through an analysis of the error before he took up the pen again.

The postscript ended with the conclusion, "You are determined to enter into retirement at the age of 67 years." He made one other point: "The word 'obviously' is in similar manner suspect as the words probably, surely, perhaps, etc."

These particular words, and such phrases as "to be frank," "to be truthful," were always suspect to Groddeck. He said they disguised something. What is obvious does not have to be called obvious. The words "probably," "surely," "perhaps," were likewise devices to protect the speaker, something like a child's crossing his fingers when he utters a lie.

The letter ended with a plea. "I would like to see you feel prompted through this discourse to occupy yourself once more with your illness and—to come to Baden-Baden."

The purpose of the long discussion was to make Freud see that in the work referred to he had made it clear that he expected to retire or to die at the age of 67, and that his present serious illness was self-punishing. Groddeck hoped to stimulate, even to anger Freud into thinking about it, and thus to stimulate or to provoke him into healing himself.

Freud, who replied to every letter, sent an answer to this one on a postcard.

> *Dear Doctor:* So you have, that is your wife, noticed something! I had been annoyed with myself all this time about the possibility of delivering a confirmation to the occult powers. It seems to have been happily avoided, I have started a new year. Best wishes for your journey.
>
> Your Freud

A good many of Groddeck's comments to Freud threw light on Groddeck himself. In one place he spoke of poor people "who can't even keep their own name." He had always had a nickname. As a child he was Pat. His patients gave him their own nicknames; "Groddie" was a favorite of the English. In *Das Buch vom Es* he is Patrik Troll. He said that the name Georg was so strange to him that every official document he signed made him feel an impostor.

He was always interested in numbers and in dates. For a long time, when he was impatient with repeating something, he would say, "I've already told you that 26,783 times." He wrote of this habit:

That vexed me and I puzzled over the mystery of this number. It occurred to me that the cross sum of the figures in this long number is 26, exactly the same number that is separated from the other figures when they are taken away. With 26 I think of my mother. I was 26 years old when my mother died. Twenty-six was the age of both my parents when they married; in the year 1826 my father was born. If you take the cross sum of the other figures, 783, you hit upon 18. Isolate the first 3 figures as $2 \times (6+7)$ and you have the 26. Add the 2 to the last two figures 8×3 and again there is 26. I was born 10/13/66. These figures can be added to make 26.

I have analyzed the number 26,783 in yet another way. The 2 seemed to me to stand by itself, since I had unwittingly applied it to the two operations with $6+7$ and 8×3. The other numbers group themselves, under the influence of the isolated 2, as 67, 78, 83. Sixty-seven was the age of my mother at the time of her death. Seventy-eight is the date I had to leave home to enter a boarding school. In '83 my old home was lost to me forever, for in that year my parents left the town where I was born, to settle in Berlin. In that same year an experience befell me, the effect of which lasted over a long period of my life . . . The year '83 has crept in as especially important in its influence upon my external existence. This corresponds to its prominent position as the end figures in the mystery number 26,783. Soon after that . . . I fell ill with scarlet fever, as a result of which I contracted nephritis. Later . . . I went through another illness of the same character.

It was no accident that Groddeck took notice of Freud's "therefores," "probablys," and such words. He took particular notice of peculiarities in writing and in everyday speech. For example, he observed, a housemaid explains that the cup broke by saying, "The handle came off in my hand." If a man has a cold he says that he has "caught" it, but if he suffers from syphilis he "is sure to accuse some wretched woman of giving it to him." And he told of a patient who was giving signs of resistance: "We took longest over getting the significance of one of my habitual phrases at that time; now and again I would use the words, 'To be frank,' or even 'I must frankly confess to you.' D. concluded from this that I was lying, which was not at all stupid of him."

It seems certain that Groddeck, in his careful analysis of Freud's article, thought he saw evidence that Freud was allowing the cancer to force his retirement. Groddeck was confident that he could help him to defeat the cancer. In a sense, of course, Freud did defeat it. He lived 16 years after the first operation and did not die until he was 83, but he underwent repeated surgical procedures, many under inadequate local anesthesia, and suffered great pain. Perhaps, according to Groddeck's theories, the suffering was enough so that Freud's It allowed him to live on.

For months after Freud's postcard, there was no further correspondence. Freud was not well enough to attend the Salzburg Congress, and Groddeck did not go either. In the summer Ferenczi came, and William Inman with him. Ferenczi brought the latest news of Freud's health, which was not good.

In December, Freud wrote asking why he had not heard from Groddeck. Groddeck replied that he had seen Ferenczi, but when he learned that Freud would not attend the congress, he lost interest in it. Even the lecture he had planned to give was put aside unwritten,

> . . . a sign that I was oriented to have you as a listener and as I find out more and more, it is you I love and not the strange atmosphere of the many Lions of Congress who are going off in all directions. I am friendly only with Ferenczi, and he is good enough to have looked me up here. Aside from that, I go along my quiet way

of practicing and adore Freud from afar. An interruption was a stay in Berlin with my wife where I gave a few lectures with a great deal of pleasure and many good results.

. . . My wife sends you her best regards and many thanks for your kind words. I myself remain as always

Your faithful student

Freud answered the letter immediately. He was not interested in personal admirers, he said, but in people to carry on the work of psychoanalysis. He knew that he had cancer, and he had not Groddeck's faith in the future. For him, the only sensible attitude was acceptance of a shortened life. He wanted very much to make Groddeck accept the organization of psychoanalysis, though he was not optimistic.

He expressed annoyance with Groddeck's tendencies toward being a lone wolf. It was a difficult, perhaps impossible, way to practice psychoanalysis, "which is an exquisitely social undertaking. Would it not be much better for us all to scream and cry together as a chorus and in the same rhythm instead of each in his corner grumbling to himself?"

He valued Groddeck's personal attachment, he assured him, but it now needed to be partly transferred to others. He was aware that Ferenczi visited Groddeck, which reminded him that his own visit had never taken place. He ended on a resigned note. Travel was now very difficult for him. Perhaps it would always remain so.

16

GENIUS OR IDIOT,
ANGEL OR DEVIL

In 1925, despite continued success in his practice, Groddeck
felt the need to do something to promote his acceptance by
the Psychoanalytical Societies. He was again putting out a
little paper, this one called *die Arche*, with essays by various
people, but its main content was furnished by him, and he was
reading a good deal with the vague urge to write something.
He had no definite idea what it should be.

In March he wrote to Freud:

> I feel a great pressure to write something and to tell
> you that I am thinking of you. The reason for the
> pressure will probably soon be apparent. The last few
> years have been busy ones for me but now things have
> become quieter. A most persistent feeling is a wish to
> determine what has developed in me as a result of my
> experiences since 1920. What form this investigation
> should take I do not know. I feel that it should not
> have the irony of *Der Seelensucher* nor the emotional-
> ism of *Das Buch vom Es*. It seems rather to be some-
> thing autobiographical. In any case, I am busily going
> over all sorts of memoirs and have a vague notion of
> doing a consciously analytical work. I suppose I should

stick to a chronological line, but I am attracted to the path of free association.

Probably that is why thoughts about you are so strong. In an analytical autobiography you would play a major role. But I am not able to proceed until I have advised you of my plan. However, I am not saying definitely that I will do such a book.

In April he wrote again. He had read Freud's short autobiography written for the Encyclopædia Britannica and reprinted as a monograph.

I have read your autobiography and gained great pleasure from it. In the final sentences, there lies so much force that I am convinced of your recovery. The whole thing leads surely uphill and he who watches and tests knows surely that the pilgrim will continue to climb with long and steady steps full of the force of life and the capacity to absorb and produce . . . A few things are going on around here . . . I am curious to know where it will lead me. Temporarily, though, I only notice from my increasingly fattening stomach that I am once more pregnant. I have a yen for the analytical. My wife is talking me into a methodical work about the It. Perhaps the whole thing will go up in smoke, and a few small articles, anyway . . . Personally it is gratifying that you have once more uttered your opinion about the qualifications of non-medicals in psychoanalytical treatment.

Freud answered this letter promptly. He was politely pleased that his autobiography had moved Groddeck, though he said it was written at the wishes of the publisher, not from any strong personal desire.

"That something is brewing within you and that it will come to some eruption I am glad to hear. As you know, I value originality even if it is connected with a certain amount of orneriness . . ."

He went on to speak of his health. "My masochism as an object of treatment has been almost consumed; it is high time that I be independent of doctors." This was the only reference Freud made to a very difficult period. His prosthesis was being changed and he could scarcely speak.

Freud received a visit from Count Kayserling in the spring. A second visit, according to Jones, turned into a consultation, and Freud recommended that Kayserling put himself into Abraham's hands. Instead, Kayserling went to Groddeck.

Kayserling, in writing of this period, says that he was suffering from "a relapsing phlebitis which other doctors had warned me would keep me an invalid for years, if not for the rest of my life." He was cured in less than a week. It does not seem likely that Kayserling consulted Freud about this symptom and there is no record of how he came to Groddeck, unless it was on Freud's advice. At any rate, Kayserling moved into the sanitarium. Groddeck's stepson, Joachim, wrote an account of the Sanitarium and Kayserling's visit.

> There was something special about this place in many respects. Groddeck, the physician, made a point of admitting only as many patients as he felt he could treat individually. He did not believe in treating his patients physically only, but took heed of their mental conditions and was aware of the fact that many of them were in need of an understanding and capable physician whom they could confide in, and tell their troubles to. Dr. Groddeck believed in the old, yet ever new, medical wisdom of healing both body and mind, and that beyond treating a physical condition or disease, the individual life of a patient should also be taken into consideration by the physician. In later years Groddeck developed a therapy of his own, based on a psychological system of treatment which according to Sigmund Freud represented a special system of psychoanalysis. Medical students of today will come

across Groddeck's name in connection with his doctrine of the "Es." He was the first medical practitioner who, in looking as deeply into the mind as into the body for cause and effect of disease, also addressed himself to the mind in a person, in his methods of treatment and healing. In his medical practice he may be considered a pioneer of what is now termed psychosomatic treatment. In many cases Groddeck's healing might almost have been called a miracle. This term, however, being an expression of an unprecise method of thinking, does not adequately explain what was actually brought about, namely, the making visible the marvelous inherent capacities of nature and being.

Graf Kayserling became very attached to his physician, and in his book, *Spectrum of Europe*, in the chapter "Germany," he expressed his admiration for him in one of the finest passages in the book. He regarded Groddeck as a friend and spiritual equal, with as great a scope of knowledge as he himself had. But contrary to Kayserling's highly philosophical nature Groddeck was exuberantly given to Eros, his life being as full of paradoxes as life itself is wont to be. Graf Kayserling was fond of this man, who had the same free and easy way with princes and the famous personages of the day as he had with people of the ordinary walks of life, an independent character who knew no social barriers or class distinction. He regarded people all alike, as human beings and scorned making a fortune out of his medical abilities. In this quest of truth he was unerring yet tolerant, always considerate and full of understanding when disclosing the weaknesses and errors from which his patients suffered. By allaying their fears he again made them fit to fulfill the demands of life. Groddeck's controversial publications had previously attracted Kayserling's attention and he had asked Dr. Groddeck to give a lecture at the "School of Wisdom." On this occasion the doctor, extemporizing in his usual unconventional manner, caused quite a stir amid the assembled "wise men of East and West" with his attacks upon maxims and doctrines, the integrity of which had never before been disputed.

Day by day these two men had long talks. In the late afternoon or toward evening you would find them sitting on one of the wooden balconies of the house overlooking the town, and enjoying the wonderful view of the Black Forest hills and of the Badener Höhe in the distance . . . With regard to many problems the two men held the same view, and also had similar likings. Groddeck loved Baden-Baden with all his heart, not only because he was engaged in the work of his lifetime there, he was also actively engaged in the development of the Spa-town. He held popular lectures on important issues, and the social views he held prompted him to found the first Cooperative Store Society. The manifold possibilities the lovely place offered appealed to him. This town was alive to urban development and at the same time enjoyed the restful beauty of a most lovely setting. The serene harmony of nature here fascinated him . . . Like Groddeck, a North German, who had chosen this place for his home, the philosopher, who had traveled in every continent, also loved Baden-Baden especially in autumn, the season during which heaven and earth shed every charm of nature upon this fair place. . . .

Izette de Forest, an American lay analyst, spent a month in Baden-Baden while the Ferenczis were visiting. "I met the Groddecks," she said, "a handsome couple . . . Because of Dr. Ferenczi's devotion to Dr. Groddeck I asked for an hour's talk with him and got it . . . I thought him most intelligent, with brilliant insight, very kind and unassuming, dedicated to his work. Dr. Ferenczi had the highest regard for him, for his therapeutic qualities and for his intelligence and insight and originality."

In June, Groddeck sent Freud copies of lectures he had given to a group of laymen. "It does not require reading. But you have a right to know what I am doing."

He asked if Freud planned to attend the Hamburg Congress. "I have announced a lecture there, and I hope that this time I shall do better in saying what I mean. However, with me it all depends on the moment at hand and much on the audience."

Freud answered, thanking him for the lectures.

> Everything that comes from you is interesting to me, even if in the details I am not always in agreement. In your Es I do not recognize my civilized, bourgeois Es, robbed of its mysticism. However, you know that mine is derived from yours.
>
> I don't think I will come to Hamburg. I must get used to quite a few sacrifices. Naturally, if I am luckier than I consider possible, then I will come.

Freud was not able to attend the congress. The paper he had written for it was read by Anna. Groddeck delivered a paper, "Psychoanalysis and the It," which contained little that was new, but was an effort to explain his views more acceptably than in his earlier lectures. The new paper was not received any better than the previous attempts. His well-wishers thought he was a great man, his antagonists were unchanged in their opinions.

Nobody seemed able to accept Groddeck with equanimity. He was either a genius or an idiot, an angel or a devil. It was impossible to find anyone to praise him faintly or damn him gently.

Years after his death a controversy arose about his height! Dr. Fromm-Reichmann remembered him as about 5'10", Mrs. Millais Culpin said he was of medium height, no more than 5'8", Dr. Michael Balint thought him well over 6 feet, possibly as tall as 6'6". Others remembered him positively, from "very tall" to "short and stocky." In fact, he was about 5′10″.

Opinions about his work were as varied, and roused more emotion than thought. Even Dr. Otto Fenichel, who was called "the encyclopedia of psychoanalysis" mis-read Groddeck. For example, in the following passage Fenichel speaks of the claims of opponents of psychoanalysis that its method is intuitive. He writes:

> Let me say, first of all, that I consider this an irrelevant proposition. Either psychoanalysis is a natural science —i.e., it works with categories—in which case its results cannot be metaphysical; or it does not concern itself with "proofs," maintaining that what is essential is the "analytic experience," and not the proofs, in which case its results would be of the same order as all professions of faith, and psychoanalysis could command no more credibility than can dogma and theosophy.
>
> There actually are some authors who do more or less hold this of psychoanalysis. Thus Groddeck writes: "When I am told that all this is nonsense, I have to accept it, but I go right on believing, even without proof, or even, possibly, *because* there is no proof; because the longer one deals with proofs, the more suspicious one becomes of them." Does not every religious man say the same of his faith?

The quotation from Groddeck, from a paper on symbolism, "Der Symbolisierungszwang" is typically Groddeckian in its enthusiasm, but it is preceded by pages dealing with the thesis that children understand symbols, that "common sense" is secured at the cost of repressing the awareness of symbols.

Fenichel was not the only author who criticized Groddeck, but Groddeck did not enter into controversy, nor would he defend himself. His friends defended him. Ferenczi never failed to acknowledge his indebtedness, even for a bit of technique, however slight. For example, at Bad Homburg, Ferenczi delivered a paper titled *Contra-indications to the "Active" Psycho-analytical Technique*—which said in part:

Alexander's [Franz Alexander] admonition which he directed against us that transference and resistance at all times are the basis of analysis was unnecessary—every beginner in analysis knows that already—but, when he is unable to mark the difference between the methods proposed by us and the much more timid methods previously in general use, it is either because for all his gifts his susceptibility to shades of difference is not his strongest point, or because in his modesty he has felt it superfluous to tell us that he was already acquainted with the suggestions we put forward. To be sure I must add that on an unprejudiced examination the credit of priority belongs to Groddeck, who when the condition of one of his patients is aggravated always comes forward with the stereotyped question: "What have you against me, what have I done to you?"* He asserted that in the solving of this question the aggravation of the symptoms could always be removed, and that also with the help of such analytic devices he was able to understand more deeply the previous history of the case. I must add that the degree of value placed on the analytic situation is only indirectly concerned with activity, and that its increased consideration in no way implies activity in my meaning of the term.

In another article, *Termination of Analysis*, Ferenczi said: "This analytic goal (no castration fear in men, full acceptance of the feminine role in women) more or less corresponds to that primeval innocence which Groddeck demands of his patients. The difference between him and me is that he

---

* See letter written to Freud in May, 1921, in reference to woman with edema.

sets out for his goal straight from the symptoms while I try to reach it by means of the 'orthodox' analytic technique, though at a slower pace."

Groddeck's paper at the congress, though it was not received with enthusiasm, did reach some members of the audience who were stimulated and enchanted. William Inman was there with Ferenczi, and was at last introduced to Groddeck, in time to hear him remark disgustedly that he would never again speak before analysts. "They have so little understanding!"

With Inman was a friend, a Miss Collins, who was ill. As Inman wrote of the event:

> Notwithstanding his [Groddeck's] disappointment at the reception of his lecture, the Congress was destined to be an important event in his life. I had taken out with me a friend, Miss M. V. E. Collins, who had been given a bad prognosis by several eminent neurologists because of well-established syringo-myelia. In my enthusiasm I thought Ferenczi could help her. He, however, quickly decided that she would do better with Groddeck, who examined, invited her to his clinic in the Werderstrasse at Baden-Baden, and there she was soon installed. A month or two later she was joined by my wife, who wished also to be treated for various symptoms by Groddeck. Miss Collins promptly began to learn German and in the following year conceived the idea of translating *Das Buch vom Es* into English. She had a gift for putting Groddeck's poetic language into good plain idiomatic English, and naturally Groddeck was delighted. Every few weeks I received installments of her manuscript, which were typed by my secretary and of course eagerly read by my household.
>
> On Miss Collins' return the usual negotiations for a publisher followed, and eventually the C. W. Daniel

Company, a firm favouring "advanced" thought, brought out *The Book of the It,* to be followed later by *The Unknown Self, Exploring the Unconscious,* and *The World of Man*—I think in that order . . . Miss Collins . . . died in 1956. Her disease certainly progressed, but over 30 years previously she had been told that in five years she would be unable to go far from home—a polite way of saying she would be virtually bed-ridden, whereas, outliving all her physicians, she travelled abroad until a few years ago. A tribute to Groddeck? I don't know . . .

It was not until several years after 1924 that I learned about Ferenczi's interest in Groddeck. Each summer he would go and stay with Groddeck in Baden-Baden, and I stayed in the vicinity, continuing my analysis there for several weeks in 1928. About then I heard that in or about 1921 Ferenczi had been dangerously ill with nephritis. The physicians could do no more for him, so he packed off to Groddeck with the result that he lived for many years and then died of some other disease. Who shall say what Groddeck's treatment did for him?

Of Groddeck himself my memories grow dim. He was a big, tall, broad-shouldered man, with blue eyes, an attractive ugly face of a Puckish kind, bald, with a clean-shaven scalp in summer, with gentle touch and strong hands (he prided himself, justly, on his skill as a masseur), a charming smile, a hearty laugh associated with a keen sense of humour, and the reverence of a mystic for the forces which carry man along the path of life. And I think he was the most humble man of science I have ever met. Approachable, kind, and deferential to high and low, shyly dignified, yet strong in faith in his views, he was a model physician. One evening in each week he held a little meeting at his Clinic to which anyone could go and bombard him with questions, and I vividly remember how his wife prompted me to be aggressive with mine—perhaps to show off his charming courtesy to a visitor . . . I cannot say anything about his relations with Freud, whom he idolised. It was rumored amongst us that when Freud sickened he was going to put himself under Groddeck's treatment, but I never knew if there was any truth in it. It never took place.

After the congress, the Groddecks visited the Ferenczis in Budapest. On November 13, Groddeck wrote from Budapest to Freud. He and Emmy would pass through Vienna on the 24th and 25th and if Freud had the "time and the desire to receive your most faithful admirer you would give him great pleasure."

In spite of the pain Freud was then suffering, he wrote Groddeck to come to see him. Only a few days before the visit Freud had surgery on his jaw to remove a retained tooth, and then further painful procedures, but when Groddeck saw him he was gracious and friendly, and the only sign of discomfort he showed was a difficulty with speech. It was a memorable visit for both Groddecks. Though Emmy considered her husband one of the world's great men, she was aware that in his eyes, Freud was the greatest of all. It was to be their last meeting, though neither knew it at the time.

17

SIXTIETH BIRTHDAY

Groddeck's carefully prepared paper, printed in the *Journal* in 1926, caused much comment. Entitled *Traumarbeit und Arbeit des organischen Symptoms* (*Dreamwork and the Work of Organic Symptoms*), it began with deceptive mildness:

Medical thinking has for decades moved in a pattern in which happenings were placed in two orders, the organic and the psychic; both were once again separated from one another by an uncertain interregnum, the nervous. This interregnum was the field of work of Freud, and in it were made discoveries which are slowly changing the world outlook of the physician . . . It soon became apparent that the facts discovered were not within the settled borders established through habit, that if one did not wish to discontinue investigation, the facts in the field of the psychical must be followed; yes, one was forced to occupy one's self with processes which had nothing to do with disease or well-being . . .

While the borderline between nervous and psychic has been imperceptibly wiped out, the one between the nervous and organic was carefully guarded. Yes, psychoanalysis rejected carefully everything which would give rise to the slightest suspicion of the organic as not belonging in its area of activity—it did this as long as possible, but this could not be maintained permanently. The old and always well-known adage that organic and psychic events were different only through classification and not by nature, finally forced its way through . . . strangely enough not in the circle of the professional psychoanalysts, who fought this off or at least pretended to be deaf, but with physicians of internal medicine, gynecology, surgery, ophthalmology, and whatever other specialities there may yet be . . . This is a pity because if one continues to treat the field of the organic as taboo, assertedly because Freud does not approve of the extension of research in this field, which is surely wrong —nobody has shown more interest in my efforts in this question than Freud—if one continues to do so the opportunity will be lost to finally bring the chaotic specialized thinking and specialized physicians under one total consideration . . .

The beginning was promising. Five years of writing and lecturing had made these ideas familiar, if not quite acceptable, to his audience. Groddeck went on to criticize Ferenczi's recent coinage of the term Bio-analysis, which "has enlarged the confusion." There was no such thing as a Bio-analysis. How can you analyze life? "Life does not let itself be analyzed, one can only speculate about life."

He spoke of the honor given him by Freud in *Das Ich und das Es* in acknowledging his indebtedness for the term *Es* and proceeded to discuss Freud's use of the term.

> . . . the concept of the Es as it was useful for my purposes was useless for him and therefore he made something different out of it than I meant . . . of the essence of psychoanalysis he has changed nothing with it, he did not add nor did he take away. It was not changed, it remained as it was, the analysis of the conscious and the repressed—precisely, the psyche. How-

ever, the Es may now be Freud's Es or mine, which
have only the name in common and can be as little
analyzed as Ferenczi's Bios . . . Something entirely
different is the question: whether one can influence the
Es with the help of psychoanalysis; and the answer to
this question is yes. Psychoanalysis, the analysis of the
conscious and the repressed can be used with great
effect in all fields of medical activity; whether this activity refers to organic or psychic or nervous occurrences, it may be used, especially where the possibility
has been given that the patient recognizes the efficacy
of these processes through his relinquishing of the resistances . . . A patient who expresses resistance in the
form of an illness of short duration cannot be analyzed.
One cannot, as Schweninger used to say, catch an express train with an ox cart . . . a fracture should not be
analyzed, one should apply a bandage and leave him to
the healing processes of the Es; however, a patient
whose fracture doesn't seem to want to heal, him one
should really analyze . . . In short, the use of analysis is a
question of efficacy, and not one of the field of illness.
It is completely unimportant for the use of psychoanalysis whether the Es has used for its expression the
organic or the psychic or the nervous form . . .

The paper then compared the dreamwork and the formation of symptoms, with careful analogy. In the dream,
there is a difference between the manifest dream content and
the latent dream content. The organic shows the same relationship between the manifest symptom and the latent processes. In dreams a fragment of reality has been transferred
into the unreal, as in external bleeding where one cannot see
the blood vessels. Symbolization in dreams should be kept in
mind when one sees symptoms—the presence of fever symbolizes hot emotions, and one will rarely go wrong in assuming
in heart disease that there is latently love-and-hate making

itself known in the picture of the symptoms.* The symptoms often present a distortion, exactly as in dreams . . . Inquiry in this field is therefore necessary and valuable because the symbols of the Es are often used under the influence of the psyche, of the unconscious and the repressed. Certain diseases, Groddeck felt, should always be treated as symbolisms—menstrual disorders, hay fever, asthma, migraine, skin disorders, etc. "One helps one's self out of logical embarrassment through the addition of the magic word nervous, but with such magic tricks one cheats . . ."

As was to be expected, Groddeck was attacked for this paper also, though the comparison between dreams and physical symptoms has never been thoroughly investigated, and would have heuristic value even today.

In the book *Dynamic Psychiatry*, published in 1952, the chapter "The Psychosomatic Approach in Medicine," written by Alexander and Szasz, contains the following paragraph:

> When psychoanalytic interest first turned to the problems of organic medicine, some pioneers, notably Georg Groddeck, attempted to understand somatic processes entirely *as if* they were the same as psychic processes and symptoms. He applied psychoanalytic concepts to physiologic processes, without due recognition of the fact that the latter require different conceptual tools for adequate description and understanding. The results thus arrived at were often bizarre, such as "interpreting" the fever of an infectious diesase as "meaning" sexual excitement, or the increased blood flow to an organ, for whatever reason, as "meaning" a displaced erection.

The sources for this paragraph are given as *The Book of the It* and the 1917 article on the psychoanalytic treat-

---

* "The presence of fever symbolizes hot emotions." This does not say that fever "means" hot emotions, as so many critics of Groddeck claim.

ment of organic disease. There is no mention of the paper on dreamwork and organic symptoms, in which Groddeck stated clearly that he believed "the symptom is not the event itself but only that which occurs simultaneously with the event . . . In the organic event there are relationships between the manifest symptom and the latent processes."

Groddeck's concept of symptoms can be easily demonstrated. When the observer sees a sudden flush on a friend's face, he is seeing a symptom. The underlying "event" may be embarrassment, anger, or shame; the "psychic event" may be conscious or unconscious or partly both. The "event" behind the hot flush of the menopause is for the most part unconscious, and the specific content is available to psychoanalytic uncovering.

Each of us recognizes the standard picture of anxiety. We see the pallor, sweating, the expression on the face. As physicians we can point to a change in the pulse rate, changed bowel activity. As human beings who have experienced anxiety we can recall the sensations in the chest, mouth, throat, and bowel. Is it so difficult to postulate that both the psychic and physical concomitants of anxiety stem from a single event?

As for the statement that Groddeck "interpreted" fever as "meaning" sexual excitement, Groddeck's words were: "The physician will do well to remind himself that in the occurrence of a fever the It has a desire for great warmth to *symbolize** hot emotions."

One does not have to agree, but in all fairness to Groddeck, one should disagree with what he says, not with what he did not say.

The same year an abstract in English of the paper *Ein Symptomanalyse* (A *Symptom Analysis*) was published in the *Psychoanalytic Review*. Groddeck had corresponded with

---

* Authors' italics.

Freud about the case years before, and Freud had recognized the patient described, saying that there could hardly be two such patients.

This was one of the first "sophisticated" analytic patients. The man had been seen by other analysts before he came to Groddeck, and had read extensively in psychoanalytic publications. He sought out Groddeck with severe recurring pains in the legs.

> Analysis revealed that the patient identified himself with his father, who was lame, and toward whom there was repressed hatred. The patient's associations were most interesting, but from his long contact with analysts and analytic literature it was clear that some of the associations were consciously chosen as symbolic.

The paper mentions that the patient who has read the literature (and this patient had obviously taken some of his symbols from Groddeck's own writings) can affect the treatment. Groddeck considered that the patient's quoting of his therapist's ideas, plus the general behavior, proved a strong negative transference. Although he was cautious in drawing general conclusions from ideas expressed by a single patient, he decided that for the treatment it is not too important whether the patient has read a thought or brought it out of his own experience. He uses it, and its significance for his unconscious is there. Much of his own repressed material crystallizes about the foreign element.

Even today there are many psychoanalysts and psychoanalytically-oriented therapists who forbid reading of psychoanalytic literature by their patients. That such knowledge may be used in the service of resistance to the analytic process is true, but it is equally true of all knowledge. As with any other form of resistance, it must be analyzed as to its unconscious meanings and sources. In general, this form of resistance proves most difficult to therapists addicted to "psychoanalese" who do not fully understand the technique they are using.

When an analyst uses the main tools of psychoanalysis, those of truly listening and observing both the patient and himself, this form of resistance yields also. So Groddeck reasoned forty years ago. Today the caution to patients against reading is becoming increasingly pointless, at least in this country, where psychoanalytic concepts have become part of present day culture.

In April, the first General Medical Congress for Psychotherapy (Die Allgemeine Arztliche Gesellschaft für Psychotherapie) met in Baden-Baden.

According to Dr. W. G. Eliasberg, who wrote an account of the six meetings of the organization for the *American Journal of Psychiatry*, the Congress set itself up to deal with the domestic and foreign policies for psychotherapy. The program was ambitious: there was to be training; post-graduate training; the establishment of a code of ethics for psychotherapists; the study of psychotherapy in its relationship to psychology and psychopathology; committees were planned on psychotherapy and clinical research, quack medicine, social medicine, labor, traumatic neuroses, social neuroses, the law, pedagogy, and religion.

In all, 537 representatives of psychotherapy, psychoanalysis, and clinical medicine from Germany, Austria, Switzerland, and Sweden attended the first congress. Thereafter, the congress met yearly until 1933, when the society came under the heel of National Socialism, and Jung became editor of the *Zentralblatt für Psychotherapie* and made his well-known and disgraceful statement: "The factual differences between German and Jewish psychology, which have long been known to intelligent people, shall no longer be wiped out, and that can only be helpful for science." That was the end of the Congress for Psychotherapy, but there had been exciting meetings in the six years it lasted.

There were many visitors in the latter part of the year. In August, Ferenczi spent a week with Freud and from the 2nd to the 6th of September, he visited Groddeck with Lou Salomé. Ferenczi was leaving for the United States on the twenty-second. Erich Fromm recalls that he was with the Groddecks and their guests one evening when Groddeck delivered a forthright attack on the method of psychoanalytical training. Ferenczi made no defense.

Lou Salomé took the opportunity of watching Groddeck "performing his magic." She was an analyst who had studied with Freud before the war. Jones said that she was a woman with a "flair" for great men and counted among her friends Turgenev, Tolstoy, Strindberg, Rodin, Rainer Maria Rilke, Arthur Schnitzler, Nietzsche, and Freud. At the Berlin Congress of 1922 she had become interested in Groddeck, and, since she was a friend of Ferenczi, she took the opportunity now of seeing the Groddecks in their own surroundings.

Groddeck questioned his guests closely about Freud, about his state of health, his disposition, the number of patients he was treating. Lou Salomé was much impressed with the results of his treatment of Ferenczi, who had not in years been well for such long periods.

Frieda Fromm-Reichmann brought a patient to Groddeck that same week, a man who had been told he had tuberculosis. The question was whether he should go to a sanitarium in Switzerland or remain in Germany for treatment. After taking a walk in the woods with the patient, and talking with him, Groddeck told Fromm-Reichmann, "If a man gets TB in order to go abroad, he ought to go abroad."

Dr. Inman paid a short visit, staying in a hotel, and joining the guests at the sanitarium in the evening. One of the patients had a birthday, and Inman described the proceedings.

"On birthdays the domestic staff would serenade outside the room door during lunch, then enter, shake hands, and give birthday greetings. The atmosphere of the sanitarium was that of a friendly family."

Die Arche was coming out regularly and was proving surprisingly popular. It had been intended for patients in the sanitarium, but many analysts asked to have their names put on the mailing list, and copies went to England, Holland, and the Scandinavian countries. Written now completely by Groddeck, it gave him a place to print the little essays that were not suitable for the medical journals or for the non-medical psychoanalytic journal, *Imago*. Some of the pieces were personal reminiscences and many were charming.

The English translation of *The Book of the It* was finished, and Miss Collins was eager to set about further translations. She turned up a little paper called, "A Sermon for Christmas," written in 1910 by Groddeck for Else's children, and still expressing his views. More than most, Groddeck's life was a tightly-knit fabric of work and recreation. To him, work meant the practice of medicine and his writing, and play was a continuation of both. "A Sermon for Christmas" says poetically and lyrically that life is a continuum.

For the late autumn in Berlin, Groddeck planned a series of lectures on the It. He wrote them with care, and Miss Collins chose five lectures to translate. Under the title *The Unknown Self*, she planned to publish the Berlin papers with several others taken from *die Arche*, as well as "A Sermon for Christmas."

In October, for Groddeck's sixtieth birthday, Freud sent a charming message by telegram. Groddeck wrote from the forest retreat to thank him.

> As far as I can judge of the mysterious nature of my It, it wills itself a long and happy life. At any rate, it is happy in the participation in your *Ich und Es*, and is proud of it.
>
> We have once more gone off on vacation after a busy year. At first to our dearly beloved hut, but we

want to go on to Berlin where I will once more give lectures, and then probably to London.

F. [Ferenczi] and Frau Andreas Salomé were here and spoke of you and your health. I accept all news which deals with the object of my latest passion most thirstily and I hold on to it.

The birthday was especially memorable because the Vienna Psychoanalytic Association sent congratulations, and the *Journal* published a tribute by Ernst Simmel.

Here was real praise from an official source, the first since Ferenczi's friendly reviews nearly twenty years earlier. True, Simmel was a devoted friend, but his tribute appeared in an official journal.

We know how Groddeck hates anything that savors of official action, even when its only purpose is to do him honour, and if we tried to thank him for the help his work has given to the psychoanalytic movement, he would certainly acknowledge such thanks only with a few ironic remarks about himself. For in his heart of hearts it is not psychoanalysis which interests him, whether as a movement or as a body of thought, but men, and in particular the man afflicted by disease.

The urge to help such a one first made Groddeck a physician and then led him to psychoanalysis, for he recognised from the first how one-sided was any treatment of organic disease which took no account of the mental life of the sufferer. By applying psychoanalytical knowledge and experience to the organic domain he opened a track between the mental and the physical, on which he has established a new method of treatment, indeed a new art of medicine. The host of prejudices which his work aroused, he encountered with the weight of his unique and original personality. Incidentally he cured many "incurables." . . . When we who are members of the International Psychoanalytic Society think of Groddeck, our minds naturally turn to that day at The Hague Congress, when he mounted the platform to announce, "I am a wild analyst." In so saying he was right, only we must not give that term its usual meaning as indicating the sort of person who, without any training, without even having grasped anything of the spirit of analysis, yet dares to treat mental disease. Groddeck may be permitted to style himself "wild"—in relation to the movement of which he is a supporter—in the sense that he owes his training to no one but himself. He may also be termed "wild" in virtue of his passionate temperament, which impels him to action where others throw up a case as hopeless or disguise their real helplessness under the cover of "accurate diagnosis." This temperament is the source of that "wildness" which, thanks to his peculiar gifts, has enabled him, a fanatic in the cause of healing, to make Freud's discoveries of service in organic illness. Groddeck's "wildness," however, is also courage, the courage to pursue one end alone, the truth, unadorned, as he sees her embodied in Freud . . . Wild, too, as we know, is the hatred with which he attacks those worn-out medical dogmas, which, with professional egotism, made the physician instead of the patient the centre of the medical picture . . . For we specialists can no longer afford to dispense with the knowledge which Groddeck passes on to us. *The Book of the It,* that series of variations on the one great theme that the whole body, sick or sound, is the instrument of the mind, a book which represents the harvest won from countless observations and devoted services to the sick, is even yet not prized by us as its wealth of therapeutic suggestions deserves . . . He has won a sure place for himself among great physicians by the boldness of his action. At a time when Freud's theories were being contemptuously boycotted in their own sphere of psychology, Groddeck accorded them full rights in the realm of physiological therapy. But here I run the risk of exciting his wrath, for long habit has led me to repeat the old distinction between the physical and the mental domain, and it has not been allowed to us to put body and mind in opposition since 1916, when he published his first pamphlet on "The Psychoanalytic Treatment of Organic Disease." . . .

Whoever, like the writer of this article, has had the good fortune to stay some days in the Marienhohe and to go for walks with Dr. Groddeck in that beautiful countryside, will recognise and admire through the opportunity he has enjoyed of coming into closer contact with his personality, the consummate artistry of his very life. All his words, written or spoken, whether they be poems or medical opinions, the whole method of his treatment, are alike expressions of an intuitive artist.

I only wish that a great many analysts could spend some days with Groddeck. They would come back to their own laborious work for the sick enriched in courage, self-confidence and willingness to undertake responsibilities, and more still they would win to a greater freedom and independence of soul in facing the tremendous difficulties of their calling.

Ernst Simmel, never himself an analysand in a formal sense, was noted for his interest in difficult cases—alcoholism, narcotic addiction, psychoses—problems which remain today the most resistant to psychoanalytic therapy.

Simmel, Deri, Horney, Ferenczi, Inman, Fromm-Reichmann, all remained loyal admirers, though never disciples. Groddeck would permit of no disciples.

Frieda Fromm-Reichmann, of whom her colleague, Dr. Edith Weigert said, "Frieda Fromm-Reichmann was a born psychotherapist," will long be remembered as one of the truly creative therapists. From the day she met Groddeck, he became for her a source of instruction and inspiration. She ranked him with Freud, Kurt Goldstein, and Harry Stack Sullivan, her teachers, to whom she dedicated her first book. *Principles of Intensive Psychotherapy* remains a classic, though it gives nothing more than a hint of the marvelously intuitive understanding and the warmth Fromm-Reichmann gave to her schizophrenic patients.

Frances Deri, considered a highly original and courageous thinker, was a warm friend of Groddeck. She describes having spent an entire day in search of a book Groddeck lacked to complete his collection of stories by Karl May, the German who wrote of the American old West. She found the volume and presented it to Groddeck as a birthday gift.

Ferenczi, who was Groddeck's grateful patient and close friend, introduced a number of concepts into psychoanalysis, some even yet controversial, some rather tentatively accepted as "parameters" of psychoanalysis. Like Groddeck, he believed that an effective interpretation to a patient must appeal to all levels of the psychic organization, but most prominently to the level of the greatest psychic investment. Thus, the confrontation with a frankfurter to a singer with laryngitis and aphonia (attributed to the late Dr. Lionel Blitzen) he would consider a true interpretation on an "oral" level rather than a parameter.

Almost without exception, those who applauded Groddeck tended to be rebels and innovators, indifferent to the opinions of others. This includes Freud himself, who was subjected to much criticism for his defense of Groddeck.

The acknowledgment of the tribute from the Vienna Society, which called for a conventional expression of gratitude and humility, brought from Groddeck something more.

> The acceptance which my concepts have found on the part of the body of the International Psychoanalytical Association are a most effective stimulus to me to investigate further the fields which lie before me, and to make those which are thus far hardly discernible accessible so that they can be fruitfully examined by the methodical sciences.

This was a barb, since he had never really been accepted by the "body" of the International Psychoanalytical Society, only by certain courageous members, and nobody knew it better.

> I hope soon to be able to revive *Der Seelensucher*, which I consider an example of my greatest skill. Laughter should not be neglected in seriousness.

The reference to *Der Seelensucher*, which caused consternation on its first appearance, as "an example of my greatest skill" was not innocent. It was a tacit agreement, clear to those who cared for him, that Groddeck had given up the search for academic approval.

18

VISIT TO ENGLAND

In 1927 a young woman from Zurich visited the Sanitarium. She came as a patient, but stayed on as a friend and helper and soon began to act as Groddeck's secretary. Fraulein Margarete Honegger became the heiress to his literary estate, and for almost forty years has guarded his books, papers and correspondence.

On his return to the continent from the United States, Ferenczi went directly from London to Baden-Baden to see Groddeck, then to Berlin to see Eitington, then back to Baden-Baden before going to Vienna. Apparently the delay in visiting Freud—three months—made Freud feel that Ferenczi was withdrawing himself. Jones was of this opinion, though Ferenczi at the time wrote Freud that nothing would ever change between them, and Freud agreed that at this late date they should not separate.

Ferenczi confided to Groddeck his troubles with Freud. In the Freud biography, Jones gives his version of the disagreement. Some of Ferenczi's students were of the opinion that his heart was broken by Freud's cruelty to him. The argument still continues. Though Groddeck was a loyal friend to Ferenczi, he also adored Freud, and he was no giver of advice. He listened to Ferenczi, listened and sympathized. He was himself having problems with Freud, which he confided to no one. He was unable to give up his fantasy of being a son to Freud, a favorite, and nothing less could ever satisfy him.

Diane Herz, who visited Groddeck at this time, described him as follows:

> In 1927 I had read his book *Das Buch vom Es* which made a deep impression on me, and as I was in Germany at the time I decided to go and see him in Baden-Baden and saw him twice. I remember him as being very tall, maybe six feet two,* and he looked as sturdy as an oak tree. His hair was then grey, his eyes piercing but kind with an impish expression. I had been told how gruff and unapproachable he was supposed to be, but to the contrary he was most kind and put me at ease as soon as we started to speak.
>
> Our discussion of some of my personal problems was most illuminating. As I left he said, "Don't make the mistake of taking psychoanalysis too literally or for that matter too seriously; don't forget that this subject is not a science, yet, but only in the embryonic state."

In September Freud wrote Groddeck with reference to the idea of illustrating a new edition of *The Book of the It*. He felt that illustrations should not be used. Groddeck replied:

> A letter from you always puts me into a good mood and I will use it to answer you right away, but this should not be considered as begging for a further letter even though I do not want to deny that it would give me pleasure.

---

* She overestimated, like many others who were misled about his size. Frieda Fromm-Reichmann probably summed it up best: "He had such presence that he seemed to fill any room he entered." She looked about at the room in which we sat, a conventional living room, something over sixteen feet in length, "In this room you would say he was a giant."

I am quite of your opinion that such books should not be illustrated, but the public sometimes has odd wishes. It could be that they would find an illustrated edition to their liking. The publisher himself will know best whether the attempt will be worth it.

That you find no pleasure in *The Book of the It* I realize . . . The expression "*It* mythology does not carry me further." I can consider a compliment as well as a reprimand.

It is the reader who decides about the value of a book and there is absolutely no sense in the author defending his own book; one knows that he considers it good, otherwise he wouldn't have published it. But you are not really a teacher, to make you responsible for the achievements of your students, and you are also not a reader in the customary sense of the word, but you are Freud and as such you might perhaps do better to consider the foolishness of your admirers with forbearance. Just as your appreciation invigorates, your reprimand kills.

When I consider the accomplishments of psychoanalytical literature in the last few years I find there the same monotony you seem to find in the Es mythology, only in a different key. Why don't you allow the same mitigating factors to me that you offer to others? Despite your rejection I have faith,* I believe that there are a number of advantages to the book which are not to be underestimated. First, the facts offered in it were true, and they are not only true for my own credulity, because I maintain for the real and the ideal truth the communications of renewed confirmations from both licensed and unlicensed physicians. Besides, the book is not boring. Thirdly, it mentions a number of things by name, which was urgently necessary, and fourthly, it

* There was, of course, no rejection. Freud had simply not praised the book enough for him.

covers a field about which I am more informed than others.

The fact that not one of the members of the Association has dared to follow my suggestion—Deutsch, and the American whose name I forget, really don't count—does not rest upon the fact that my way is wrong. There are enough people outside of the Association who are trying hard to find on the corpus vile of the patient clarification of what Freud has meant and who will no longer let themselves be shackled in the inner circle of the neuroses. I cannot free myself of the thought that this remarkable behavior of the Association lies rooted in the fear of your disapproval. One knows what you think of *The Book of the It*, but one does not know, or at least one pretends that one doesn't know what you think of the use of psychoanalysis in the organic. I am vain enough to draw a conclusion from your years and years of silence about my activity, which may be expressed thusly: This Groddeck might have a useful idea, but the manner in which he introduces it, I, Freud, cannot approve. He must and therefore will help himself alone. This is very honorable for me, but it hurts long and deep.

Please remember us both to you and yours and for you the most reverent of greetings from me and my wife.

Your devoted student

Everything is openly revealed in this letter. If Freud ever answered it, there is no copy of his reply. Groddeck was bitter about the expression "It mythology." Perhaps he had heard it from Ferenczi, in an indiscreet moment. Though he was not a gossipy man, it is conceivable that Ferenczi said something to prove that Freud treated his followers badly. It was a painful thought to Groddeck, and he reacted to it. Though it did not spoil his regard for Freud, it interrupted their correspondence. He did not write again to Freud until 1930.

Groddeck had a good many English patients in the Sanitarium; there were always tourists who had heard of him and wanted to have a look at him and a talk with him. The English publication of his *Book of the It*, which was already in a second edition, had given him a reputation there. He was invited to address the British Psychological Society, and he accepted, arranging to give a talk on November 28. He planned to lecture on the case of Frau A., the old lady with renal colic, who had first consulted him in 1901 when he treated her with violent massage, and who lived to enjoy the "psychic treatment."

The visit to England was memorable. The Groddecks were guests at Meads, the Culpins' country home. Mollie Collins, the translator, and May Smith, the psychologist, came to spend a weekend during the visit. One night, according to Mrs. Culpin's recollection, "Frau Groddeck went to Mollie's bedroom and presented her with a magnificent jewelled pendant given to Frau Groddeck by Groddie.* I know he appreciated very much all Mollie's translations and Frau Groddeck appreciated her initiative in introducing her husband's book to England. He was a perfect dear! I was very fond of him; he was so simple and single-minded, really like a big baby at times. He could not suffer fools gladly, as I found when I put him next to ____ one night, thinking ignorantly that being German he would feel more 'at home.' Poor woman—he withered her."

Dr. Culpin was asked by Dr. Flugel to bring Groddeck up to London for dinner. A number of others were invited to meet the visitor, "and as usual the men discussed and argued many points in their work with some excitement, whilst Groddeck sat quietly, looking rather sad; he thought they were all quarrelling and told Mill that 'that couldn't happen in Germany.' When Mill explained, he laughed and thought it was

* In that group, Groddeck was Groddie, and his wife Froddie.

wonderful that scientists could contradict each other flatly—
even the host—and yet be friends." He never forgot that dinner.

At the Flugels' dinner, Mrs. Culpin told Groddeck she
was giving him a new nickname, Nick—"he sometimes
looked like the pictures of my childhood days of 'Old Nick'
with his outstanding ears," and he loved it. "He was writing a
book when with us," Mrs. Culpin remembered, "and showed
me the manuscript, but said, 'I can't decide on a title.' After
reading it, I said, 'I have a title for you, The Unknown Self.'
This pleased him, he used it, and I was given the first published copy."

No doubt Groddeck had a manuscript with him, but *The
Unknown Self* was a compilation, selected by Mollie Collins
from various sources, and not an original manuscript. He
wrote nothing new for it; the chapters were translations from
previous writing.

On another occasion, May Smith gave a dinner at her
club before a meeting. Lord d'Abernon was in the chair. For
the first time, Georg Groddeck was a celebrity, a gratifying
role, and somehow resulting in his becoming more and more
comfortable, more childlike and open. He won everybody he
met; nobody considered him odd or difficult; he seemed to be
in his element.

At another dinner party during the stay in London, William Inman recalled, "the guests were having sherry in the
drawing room. A well-known psychologist was present who
had just published a book that had been reviewed critically
because of the neglect of the endocrine glands. Dr. Culpin
went up to the author and said, 'It's a pity you don't know
about the endocrine glands.' The writer, a fairly good actor,
put on a sad face and said, 'But I did put them in the appen-
dix.' Groddeck turned to his partner and asked, 'Won't Professor X be hurt by Dr. Culpin?' 'Of course not,' he was told,
'he knows it's a joke.' Groddeck shook his head and said ad-

miringly, 'You English! How do you know when you are joking?' "

There were distinguished people present both at the dinner party and at Groddeck's subsequent lecture—Major Greenwood, a gold medallist of the Royal Society, Culpin, and many others. The lecture was well received; indeed the entire trip was an unforgettable experience for Groddeck.

19

"MOST HONORED TEACHER AND MOST DEARLY BELOVED MAN"

The Society for Psychotherapy, completely destroyed a little later by Jung under Hitler, ran into censure in January, 1930. At a meeting of the German Psychoanalytical Society, Ernst Simmel, as an officer, read a statement which declared that the German Psychoanalytical group was obliged to disclaim any responsibility for the Psychotherapy Society. The ostensible reason was the ill-defined "line" the new society planned to take with regard to psychoanalysis.

As a consequence, the psychoanalysts of Southwest Germany who had hoped for stimulation and mutual education from the new group, began to meet informally and irregularly in Heidelberg, in the apartment of Frieda and Erich Fromm. Frieda Fromm-Reichmann went to great trouble to make the meetings agreeable to Groddeck, and had conferences with Emmy about the food to be served to him. The Fromms had been guests in the Groddeck home, and Emmy was a hostess who took especial trouble over her guests' preferences. For Groddeck, food presented no problem; he had a hearty appetite, and as long as everything was well-prepared, he had few dislikes. He liked strong tea and strong coffee; he drank no alcoholic beverages except beer and wine, and he preferred

Rhine wine with meals. He was addicted to American ciga-
rettes, which Dr. Fromm-Reichmann always kept in supply
when she expected him.

In April, a congress of the Arztliche Gesellschaft für
Psychotherapie met in Baden-Baden, attended by Simmel and
Ferenczi among others. Ferenczi made reference to his debt
to Groddeck in a paper—"Principles of Relaxation and
Neocatharsis" prepared for the congress and printed in the
October issue of the *International Journal.*

> The relaxation-technique which I am suggesting to you
> assuredly obliterates even more completely the distinc-
> tion between the analysis of children and that of adults
> —a distinction hitherto too sharply drawn. In making
> the two types of treatment more like one another I was
> undoubtedly influenced by what I saw of the work of
> Georg Groddeck, the courageous champion of the psy-
> choanalysis of organic diseases, when I consulted him
> about an organic illness. I felt that he was right in
> trying to encourage his patients to a childlike naïveté
> and I saw the success thus achieved.

The Dresden Congress for Psychotherapy in August included lectures by Simmel, Horney, Michael Balint, Fromm
and others, as well as several remarkable lectures by Groddeck.

He delivered a paper on "Struelpeter," the gruesome
nursery rhyme. One sequence tells of a disobedient little boy
who went out with an umbrella in the rain and blew away.
This was "flying Robert." (Groddeck had often called his eldest brother by this name.) Erich Fromm recalls that the talk
was full of original ideas and startling insights.

After the Congress, Simmel and several others remained
in Baden-Baden as guests of the Groddecks for several days.
Groddeck asked everyone about Freud. Did Freud ever speak
of him? How did he look? Was there any sense in inviting him
to Baden-Baden for a rest?

It was about this time that Groddeck suffered what may have been a stroke, though it was called a heart attack. It was similar to the illness suffered by his father. Unlike his father, he allowed his frightened wife to call a physician. He was ordered to rest, warned that he must give up drinking and smoking. He had no intention of giving up either. As soon as he felt better, he again ordered wine with his meals and began to smoke. Emmy reminded him that he had been strongly advised not to smoke. He looked at her and smiled. "I know," he said, "but that's not my way."

On September 1st, after nearly three years of estrangement, he read in the paper that Freud had been awarded the Goethe prize for literature. Anna Freud accepted it for her father with a speech at the Goethehaus in Frankfurt. Freud sent Groddeck his photograph, and Groddeck was delighted. He sat down to write, found himself still too shaky and took to the typewriter. He began with the salutation, *My most honored teacher and most dearly beloved man*:

> Owing to the fact that I have reason to distrust the legibility of my handwriting, you will excuse me if I use the typewriter instead of the pen . . . Your picture gives me great joy and is a surprise such as has rarely happened to me. I did not suspect that you knew what you personally mean to me.
>
> Unfortunately I heard too late that you have been awarded the Goethe prize. From what I have heard, there are quite a few people who feel the necessity of commenting upon it. If I may judge from my own experience there could not be anyone in the whole world who would have earned it more. I was brought up in the admiration of Goethe, but I did not understand much of him until I became acquainted with psychoanalysis. Based on the assumption that psychoanalysis is no longer a medical affair but something quite different, I am enabled to put questions. I now turn to you, the new careful guardian, in the hope that you may yet say something to the boy of the very best that you know.

When Faust, after his death, is carried upward by angels, some verses accompany this action about which the student has fantasized until he felt that wheels were going around in his head. What disturbs me are the indications which the words include, "he who strives forever more, him we can deliver . . ." According to the report of Eckermann, Goethe told him that the puzzle of Faust is solved in these verses. As little as I—from family tradition—trust Eckermann, I still cannot assume that he might have heard wrongly, especially since in connection with this he gives a long account of what Goethe was further supposed to have said of it, but this sounds like true Eckermannish . . . The quotes prove that the famous words from "of this striving" is a quotation and not merely reflecting an opinion of the angels . . .

I do not intend to tempt an answer from you with this question. I would much rather that you would refute me. As much as I would like Goethe to be the crown's witness of my weird ideas, I would still fear it in my Godlikeness.

The best might be not to answer at all, but the best is not always the most pleasant for your somewhat aging student,

Groddeck

Please tell Fraulein Anna how sorry I am not to have welcomed her in Frankfurt. I trust she has a forgiving heart.

Freud did not attach any significance to the difficulty with handwriting. Nor did Groddeck mention his illness. He was in his old, favorite relationship: the son, the pupil, the humble questioner.

Freud replied from Grundlsee, where he was resting. He said that he was not obliged by convention or courtesy to acknowledge congratulations on a public achievement. Quite apart from congratulations, however, Groddeck's letter contained other things which he enjoyed.

When I am in Vienna again and near my bookcase I shall try to figure out the place to which you object. I will look into Eckermann, who is as unsympathetic to me as to you, and then I will write to you about it.

Meanwhile I don't understand Goethe in that any better than I do Groddeck . . .

In January of the following year, at a meeting at Frieda Fromm-Reichmann's apartment, Groddeck spoke on English literature. Later in the year he wrote a paper, "The Influence of English Literature upon Germany." Actually, he meant by "English literature" works written in the English language. The article started like a story.

> Once upon a time, it might have been well over 50 years ago, there stood upon a sandpile in the middle of his father's yard, a little German boy of about eight. Upon his head he wore a home-made paper helmet circled by a crown fashioned of gold paper. In his right hand he held a wooden sword, and, brandishing this weapon, he cried to his playmates, "A horse, a horse, my kingdom for a horse!" There happened along his bigger and much older brother, who laughed and exclaimed, "Well, you are a cute king." "Cute?" asked the boy in amazement, "No, Richard, Richard III, and this is a tragedy by Shak-es-pierre, for your information." Thereupon the brother laughed only more loudly and said, "The man's name was Shakespeare and he was an English poet." The little one bit his lips in order not to cry and then full of anger he spat out the following words: "I know that Shakespeare was an Englishman, but I am not talking about him. I am talking about Shak-es-pierre, who was a German and who wrote his tragedies in German. How else would I be able to read them?" Whereupon the older says, "You are and always will remain a dumpkopf. This play is by the greatest English dramatist and has been translated by Schlegel into German. Just look in the book, which

says 'translation' on the first page." For a while the little king stood motionless upon his sandpile and then he threw down his crown and sword and ran into his father's library. There he sat for a long time and looked upon the words, "Translated by F. Schlegel," and the tears ran down his cheeks just because Shakespeare was an Englishman and not a German.

This story is true and we in Germany feel exactly like him. For us Shakespeare is just as German as the Bible and since Bible reading has gone out of fashion, Shakespeare's works mean still more to us than they did formerly.

Shakespeare was Groddeck's great love, but his other favorites in English were curious. Richardson's *Clarissa* he called "the root of all German novel writing and the basis of romantic literature." He assumed that Goethe received inspiration for *The Sorrows of Werther* from *Clarissa*. *The Sorrows of Werther* accompanied Napoleon in his campaigns, "a nice example of how one genius understands another even though their fields of activity lie on different planes."

Goldsmith was another author dear to Germany, said Groddeck. Five books were to be found everywhere in Germany—*The Bible, Grimm's Fairy Tales* and the *Struelpeter,* and two English books—*Robinson Crusoe* and Cooper's *Leatherstocking Tales*. There were many imitations of Cooper's *Leatherstocking Tales*, as there were of *Robinson Crusoe*. Even Freud,

> . . . who with his unusual force of self-limitation has been able to force his remarkable gift of prophecy into a relatively small field of endeavor, has himself fallen prey to the magic of Defoe's tales. Already in his earliest communications about the doings of the unconscious he speaks of the interaction of Eros and fire. He crossed over with this into the self-imposed boundaries of the unconscious, and before he incorporated the concept of the Es into his teachings, forced one of his

students to toy with the ideas for many years, which found a temporary conclusion in the writing of *The Book of the It*. The author of this book which in itself has only doubtful value but has to all appearances worked like a weed on a coral island, has never discussed *Robinson Crusoe* with Freud, and therefore cannot state whether the great discoverer of the human soul was brought to his remark about fire and drive through the English adventure book; but of myself I can state that my concept of the Es as well as my opinions about the force of symbols of human life has one of its many roots in *Robinson Crusoe*.

As to Cooper,

One of the reasons that I would not go to America today is that disappointment would be too great not to encounter herds of buffalo and not to find Indians with tomahawks and scalps, covered leggins and moccasins; to have to outwit and fight them and no longer to have the opportunity with a long musket to chase a bullet into the neck of a bottle or to shoot at a potato which has been thrown up in the air and hit only its skin, or to rescue a stolen maiden from the hands of the wild ones, to liberate her from the stake of martyrdom. Such disappointments would be too great . . . Cooper and the thousands of his imitators have put a spell on me . . . In our innermost secret hearts we Germans are children, a people of dreamers who live in a world other than that of reality.

Groddeck's favorite contemporary writer was Karl May, a German who never left Germany but wrote adventure stories of American pioneers.

As opinionated in this area as in medicine, Groddeck said that the influence of English literature was diminishing considerably and that the Russians, Tolstoi and Dostoievsky, were becoming fashionable, though literature in general was declining. One man who had hardly an equal was Dickens, "in truth the creator of all modern writing." He did not compare, of course, with Shakespeare, but in his own way he was unique . . . "Dickens is from head to toe an Englishman, and so I end with a true Englishman just as I started with the German poet, Shak-es-pierre . . . Recently I read that someone has translated Shakespeare again. Why must he be translated again? For us in Germany he is a German. For the Swedes he is a Swede, and therefore it would be quite in order if the English would consider him an English poet."

It is a pity that the entire article was never published. Delicately humorous, perceptive, admiring without awe, Groddeck was interested but not overwhelmed. One thing his admirers tend to forget is that he did not take himself as seriously as they did. Laughter was more important than being correct.

In February, 1932, Groddeck wrote again to Freud. He did not mention his recent illness, but from their many mutual friends, Freud undoubtedly knew the state of Groddeck's health as Groddeck always knew how Freud was getting on.

He had not been idle during his long convalescence, but had been writing steadily. He told Freud he was now working on a book, *Das Mensch als Symbol,* and enclosed part of the manuscript, though he said he did not want Freud to trouble himself to read it.

> . . . I do not expect that you will concern yourself with the material of the enclosed manuscript, but perhaps Miss Anna Freud has just a little in memory of our meeting at The Hague of which I think not infrequently.* I would like to ask her to sacrifice a leisurely hour and to give you a short report.
> I find myself in approximately the same position as I

---

* It sounds almost as though he had forgotten that she disliked him. Actually, he knew of her antipathy from Freud himself.

was at the time of the *Seelensucher*; naturally I do not know if you can help me at this time. It would be thinkable that you might be of the same opinion as I, that the material which I am working on should better be published as the opinions of the somewhat sickly Thomas Weltlein. However, I lack the time, and probably for the rest of my life, the strength to tell stories and to formulate them, and so I have chosen the serious way.

It concerns a book in which the peculiarities of language and formative art are used to prove how tightly knit together symbol and life have forever been; the connection with medicine will, especially in the first part, be only general; at the same time I will, however, either in a complete volume in itself or in single pamphlets, discuss the working of the symbol, and the organism as a whole and its separate parts. Of both plans I am enclosing a sample which will probably suffice to enable one to decide whether the psychoanalytical publisher will allow himself to become involved in this matter. The first chapter has been taken by Storfer for the Psychoanalytical Movement and will probably appear in the next edition. I enclose the two following chapters—of the second part, the fragments about vision will give an indication. Everything is still unready and requires working over. I hope to complete the first part in the fall and to have a considerable part of the second in readiness.

That I submit the work to you in the form of a monster instead of waiting until the brat has become respectable has its reason in the uncertainty whether the *Verlag* could decide in principle if it would want to publish this work. Out of this no obligation should arise. It is merely a question. Since I know from experience how long it takes if one peddles a completed manuscript among publishers, I shall try at least to start things.

Storfer has informed me that he will leave the

V*erlag* on the 1st of April. If I have understood correctly, your son will take his place. I have at the same
time given him notice of this step just as I have done
with you. I hope he will have the kindness to send back
the manuscript at his convenience whether I receive a
yes or no answer. With my regards and wishes, your
unfortunately somewhat senile and feeble but still
grateful student.

The economic situation in Germany was precarious, and
the V*erlag* was going through a financial crisis so serious that
its very survival was questionable. Freud had, as a last resort,
decided to issue an appeal to the International Psychoanalytical Association to take responsibility for the V*erlag* from that
time forward.

Anna Freud answered Groddeck for her father, who had
insisted on reading the manuscript himself. "He wants me to
tell you that he never did believe in your mental infirmities or
senility, but especially not after reading this material."

Unfortunately, the letter went on, the V*erlag* was in a
serious financial position, causing it to limit publication to
those journals and books for which the authors could pay the
costs of publication. She said that she was very sorry, but
there was no other way to keep the publishing house operating. "My father sends his best regards. He is well, he is over-
coming all physical difficulties which he encounters with always renewed energy and vigor."

Groddeck himself was fully recovered, and on March 6
spoke at a meeting in Heidelberg on "Vision"—his favorite
topic. Later in the spring he visited England and delivered, in
English, his paper on English literature.

20

LAST DAYS

Ferenczi wrote from Budapest:

> Physically I am relatively well. Mentally, at times I am most active and at times exceedingly tired. The things with which I occupy myself are still not ripe for communicating. My "scientific fantasy" which, however, is "well-disciplined" (Freud) leads me into excursions far beyond the unconscious, at times to the so-called metaphysical, at least so far as it repeats itself with comparative uniformity in the productions of patients. From the dreams seems to open up a way to the deeper understanding of the splitting of the personality, as well as the psychoses. I am indebted for the technical advances to the signposts which patients give through their own resistances.
>
> The newest thing here is the starting of a psychoanalytical ambulatorium in which the Family K. is actively working. The Congress has been postponed to the end of August, but I believe it will not be held even then.
>
> Frankly admitted, I sometimes envy you, dear Pat, for your illness. How lovely it must be to rest in your little house and garden. I hope that even these few lines will suffice to make you remember us. I hope we will soon receive good news.
>
> Financially I am not particularly well off, either.

I am only earning about half of what I received in the last years, but in view of the general downward trend this doesn't seem quite so bad. With much love and best wishes to both of you,

Your Sandor

The Congress was held in Wiesbaden, in September, and Simmel went to Baden-Baden afterwards to spend two weeks with the Groddecks before leaving for the United States. Next, Karen Horney came to say goodbye before she emigrated.

This was the period Jones describes as being difficult for Freud because of the "progressive deterioration in Ferenczi's mental condition." According to Jones, Ferenczi prepared a paper for the coming Congress and read it to Freud and Brill. Freud did not like the paper and asked Ferenczi not to read it. Brill, Eitington, and van Ophuijsen thought "it would be scandalous to read such a paper before a psychoanalytic congress." Jones advised that it be read. It was read, apparently without scandal.

At the Congress, Ferenczi confessed to Jones that he was suffering from pernicious anemia, "but hoped to benefit from liver therapy." With Groddeck so recently recovered from illness, he did not consult him about his own problems, but immediately after the Congress went to the South of France to rest. He became so ill that he shortened his vacation and went home.

Jones says that in March, 1933, "the disease, as it sometimes does, attacked the spinal cord and brain, and for the last couple of months of his life he was unable to stand or walk; this undoubtedly exacerbated his latent psychotic trends . . . Ferenczi's last letter to Freud, written in bed May 4, showed that he was much disturbed mentally, with delusions about Freud's supposed hostility. Toward the end came violent paranoic and even homicidal outbursts, which were followed by a sudden death on May 24."

There is no sign of such mental disturbance in the letters Ferenczi wrote to Groddeck in his last months. On March 20, he wrote, after he was supposedly paralyzed:

> One can obviously not sin for many years without punishment. My being unwell in Baden-Baden was the beginning of a rather dangerous anemia which almost overpowered me in France so that only with great difficulty was I able to drag myself home just in time. Since then I work under half steam and they are feeding me subcutaneously with liver. My condition is since then halfway satisfactory with only a few changes. The psychical cause of the downfall was, aside from exhaustion, also the well-known-to-you disappointment in Freud. The exchange of letters between us has since been interrupted even though we are both trying hard to save that which can be saved. I think that in the end this might still be halfway successful. I am, as always, full of ideas, but the desire to write it down is equally nil. A short, complete rest should give me some strength, but where can I go in these depressing times?
>
> I admire your perseverance and your enthusiasm despite illness and difficulty not to let your courage fail you. Your new books, whose contents were quite familiar to me, encounter great interest in all to whom I give them to read. I begin to believe that your will power will overcome all difficulties . . . I would also like to inform you that this letter has been the first after a long time which brings me in contact with the outside world, which is probably a sign of unbreakable friendship between us . . .
>
> Your old Sandor

He wanted to have Groddeck care for him, but even had Groddeck been completely well, Ferenczi, a Jew, would have had difficulty entering Germany. Nor could Groddeck have gone to him. Hitler was in power, travel was much restricted, and systematic persecution of Jews was going on.

At Heidelberg, the Southwest German analysts met in December at the home of Frieda Fromm-Reichmann. Groddeck spoke on "Body and Mind." The occasion was gloomy. The stoic ability to ignore a war was not enough for the times. Freud and Groddeck had not even acknowledged the First World War in their letters, but the situation now was different.

In May came news of Ferenczi's death. Lou Salomé wrote to Gisela saying that it was a pity Ferenczi could not have been cared for by Groddeck. "Groddeck would have saved him." In December, Gisela Ferenczi wrote to Groddeck:

> I have written to you how ill Sandor returned from his trip in the fall, but he recovered quickly and the four winter months passed in work and without trouble. In March he was already so weak that he had to stop giving lessons and we thought that a long rest until September would help him out of this weakness. Unfortunately, his illness, pernicious anemia, does not know mercy, and he became weaker and weaker . . . He lay in bed for four weeks. On the 22nd of May, the day he died, he still spoke with us, read the paper (which repeatedly fell from his hands) and he called S. to him to tell her: "It will be revised."

Those were Ferenczi's last days as described by his wife. His stepdaughter says that he noticed the first symptoms of the disease in spring, 1932.

> We found he became pale, noticeably so. Once in a while when he passed a mirror, he exclaimed: "I wonder why I am so pale—old age, I guess," and laughed. At that time he felt no discomfort and consulted no doctor. Later he got easily tired, often felt exhausted, yet, as he liked to go for a walk after dinner, with either my mother or with me, we kept up this habit for a time. His condition became perceptibly worse during

the fall, 1932. Yet he attended the International Psychoanalytic Congress at Wiesbaden in September. From there he and my mother went to Biarritz, France, for their vacation, but he could not enjoy it because he felt very, very weak. They did not write us about this bad turn as they did not want to frighten the rest of the family and they were also hoping that it was only a passing condition . . . I do not remember what treatments he got, but he recovered his energy to a great extent and soon started to work with his patients . . . He tried not to change his way of life, and even accepted invitations, though he sometimes walked with difficulty . . . He worked with a few of his patients up to a month before his passing. He spent his last two weeks in bed and in the last days he had to be fed. The food was given to him by a maid whom he liked very much. Up to the last day he joked with her. She asked him if he would like some coffee. When she returned with it he was dead. I think he would have liked to consult Dr. Groddeck in his last illness. I remember, in fact, that he talked about it. But by that time he was unable to travel, the consultation was postponed—and then it was too late.

This account was written twenty-five years after Ferenczi's death, yet it differs in only a few details from Mrs. Ferenczi's account.

Ferenczi was not homicidal nor violent, as Jones suggested. If he had flights of fancy, they were not apparent in the letters that are available. His family noticed no change in his mental condition. There would have been no point in Mrs. Ferenczi's writing a false account to Groddeck, her husband's old friend. Yet Jones was certainly not presenting a false account. There seems to have been some great misunderstanding. Probably it will never be straightened out. Ferenczi's friends continue to believe that Freud broke Ferenczi's heart.

Jones believed Ferenczi was insane when he accused Freud of hostility.

Groddeck had a different view. On February 19, 1934, he wrote to Gisela:

> I have thought for a long time whether I should write this letter and I am now determined to do so. The fact that I am writing with the typewriter is for the reason that I can only in this manner make my communication matter of fact.
>
> These last few years I have only been able to think of Sandor's life with a heavy heart. He became a victim of his spirit of scientific investigation, a fate which has been spared to me only by my own lack of thirst for knowledge. I must first speak of myself. Even before I went on to psychoanalysis there was as a basic in my medical thinking the conviction that in the human being, aside from the psyche with which science occupies itself, there exist thousands and millions of more or less independent inner lives which group themselves sometimes this way, sometimes another, working together or in opposition, and are even quite independent at times. With this conclusion I have satisfied myself and I have never tried to study this cosmos. It just isn't in my nature to concern myself with things which I consider inexplicable.
>
> In my close friendship with Sandor I noticed relatively early that he judged these things similarly, but with shock, I saw then that he was about to search in the world of man scientifically, even if possible to picture it so that one could take part in this, one might also call it drama. This striving became overpowering with him. To me he used the expression, "I atomize the soul." However, such atomizing, when it is attempted seriously, can only end with self destruction, because the other man is and will remain to us a secret; we can only atomize our own soul and that destroys us. The form in which Sandor, whose genius and bravery I

have always admired, was finally delivered of the pains of a superhuman struggle is quite beside the point. I tried every now and then to point out the dangers of his ways to him; but just as one cannot stop a raging storm with a bare hand, so I could not help Sandor. When someone says that I might have been able to do it, then is this a mistake? As close as we were, he was already far removed from me in a flight to the stars which I could not and would not join.

I cannot tell you more. The outer happenings in the life of this rarest of men have only had meaning in the way that they pointed out that he belonged to the givers who gave again and again and again.

Gisela replied a week later:

Your letter, Dear Pat, has excited and moved me deeply. I can see from it that you also needed quiet and reflection before you wanted to answer me and to make your standpoint clear to me. Perhaps it was ill-considered of me to quote Lou Salomé's words to you. I had never thought that you would read from those quoted words anything other than the great trust in your knowledge which I share with her, and I was glad that she believed in you so firmly and that she honored you, so that I rushed to repeat her words to you.

The experiences of these last years have shown me that nobody, not even you, could help him. There was a change in him which not only destroyed his body slowly, but also had a great influence upon his psychic life. His "flight to the stars," which you call it so well, flung him to such distances that he himself did not know where the final end was. From this, his desperate searching, his battle with science and conscience, his continually lasting doubts of that which already had been discovered, all this undermined his health in body and soul and caused his destruction. Would you not think that his diseased and with-time-destroyed kidney added to this? If ever someone helped in his battle, it was you, who could be master of yourself for so long. You yourself know how refreshed he always left you, how well he felt with you, and no one had such a long-lasting influence on him as you, my dear Pat. Don't you ever believe that I would wish to reprimand you even in the slightest. Deep in my heart I only have love and gratitude for you, not only that you were always able to help Sandor medically, but that you, as no other, have loved him, recognized him, and honored him. For him and me those were happy, joyful, and successful days which we spent in your midst.

Groddeck, despite the Hitlerian outrages, despite the knowledge that some of his dearest friends were, as Jews, forced to flee the country, refused to believe that Hitler was anti-Semitic. He was convinced that it was not Hitler, but evil men around him who were responsible. He wrote a letter to Hitler and described the situation. When there was no answer, he wrote again. He tried to use influence to get a letter to him, sure that Hitler had only to be informed and then everything would be well. His stubborn, childish belief was that Germany needed a leader, and that Hitler could make a great leader, but was misled. He, Groddeck, was going to set him right.

A week after Gisela's letter, a note came from Freud, the last. It was a short letter, thanking him for two articles sent for *Imago*, with a line about the state of Freud's health. "The cancer unfortunately is much closer to me, but what you say about it seems to me too uncertain, probably it does so to yourself, too."

In May, Groddeck was prostrated by another severe heart attack, and his friends tried to persuade him to leave the country. Emmy was warned that Groddeck was in danger of arrest, that he must stop trying to reach Hitler and above all he must stop his open criticism of the regime. Emmy could not persuade Groddeck that Hitler was not sincerely struggling for the good of the country. At length, there came an unmistakable warning. He would be arrested at any time.

Through the efforts of Frieda Fromm-Reichmann, the Swiss Psychoanalytical Society invited him to lecture, and he agreed. He went with Emmy to Zurich, though it had been only two weeks since his last heart attack. He spoke on a topic titled, *Eyes, Vision, and Vision Without Eyes*, the same subject, always his favorite, as his first psychoanalytical talk twenty-four years before, to the Congress at The Hague.

He was magnificent. Those who saw and heard him said he seemed a giant, a superior being. There was about him an aura of radiance that nobody could account for, as though all his forces had blazed up in final dazzling power. A few hours afterward, he collapsed, and was taken to a sanitarium at Knonau.

He gave no indication of waning strength; indeed, he seemed to be possessed of endless energies. He planned great things, a treatment which could rid the whole German nation of cancer. For his plan he needed Hitler's cooperation. Frieda Fromm-Reichmann, who visited him to say goodbye before her move to the United States, was greeted warmly, then made to take pencil and paper, while he dictated his important message to Hitler.

"Write, Frieda. The nurse won't take dictation from me. This must be written."

For hours Frieda took dictation on his cure for cancer. When it was time for her to go to the train, he said he would walk with her. She protested that he was not fit; he said that was nonsense.

"Nobody knows better than I how I feel," he said. For twenty minutes they walked on a dirt road that climbed up and down, and when they reached the station, he was not even short of breath. He stood and talked, and when the train arrived he clasped her hand and looked down at her with burning eyes. They both knew they would never meet again. He said, "All good things to you, Frieda," pressed her hands, and turned and walked away.

A few days later he was dead.

A eulogy appeared in the *Journal*, followed in the next issue by an epilogue to correct a mistake. The mistake, naturally enough, was in the origin of the term *Das Es*. It was at first credited to Goethe, and then to Nietzsche. Freud's letter, with the statement that he took *Das Es* from Groddeck before they met, was reprinted.

Then there was gossip. Stories began to circulate, especially in the United States, that Groddeck had committed suicide. When the *World of Man* appeared later in the year, there was an essay by Medard Boss, who had cared for Groddeck in the sanitarium in his last days, which seemed to say that he had died in his sleep. Frieda Fromm-Reichmann said that when she last saw Groddeck he was psychotic, though in touch with reality on many levels. He was agitated, aware that he was seriously ill, obsessed with the idea that he must write out all his ideas because death was imminent.

> People have described him as a physician who burst like a storm into the souls of men, penetrating into the depths where all life is one, all boundaries are broken down, and body and mind are fused together. There as a true creator in the dark realm of the It he shaped new life and new forms. His great knowledge and his impressive power drew many of the best minds around him, drawn as though by enchantment into the circle of his influence. Remote and proud in his hillside town, he would smile at the meaningless hurry and bustle of the busy world, yet he was always conscious of being at the mercy of forces greater than the self he knew, the forces of the It.
>
> And at last these same forces with which he had wrestled all his life overpowered him and dragged him

down into the abyss of death. His heart gave out while he slept. On his dead face there rested nothing but kindliness and a great calm.

So spoke Medard Boss over the body of Georg Groddeck. Too solemn, Groddeck would have said, much too solemn.

POSTSCRIPT

Several commentaries were written on Groddeck's work in the early fifties, more than during the whole of his life. In 1950, in a review of the book *Psychoanalysis Today*, Oskar Pfister said, "The psychosomatic illnesses . . . Have been covered by three special examinations of Jeliffe, Dunbar, and English. In a remarkable manner the founder of this highly important branch of medicine, Georg Groddeck, has not been thought of with even one syllable."

How times change! It was Pfister who wrote angrily to Freud that the *Verlag* should never have published Groddeck's novel.

In 1951, thirty years after its first publication, *The Book of the It* was reviewed by Alexander Bromley in the *International Journal of Psychoanalysis*. The review explained that Groddeck's *It* is very different from the Id of accepted psychoanalysis, that the *It* is mysterious, hazy, and ambiguous.

Curiously, on the same page, Michael Balint reviews *Exploring the Unconscious* and *The Book of the It*. Dr. Balint says:

> Two old and dear friends in a new form changed from German into English. *The Book of the It* is one of my favorite books, perhaps the very first writing in medi-

cine that took seriously the idea that illnesses which impress us as somatic or organic are caused by emotions, in fact are un-understood or misinterpreted expressions of emotions. The form chosen to convey this message to us is that of letters written by a doctor, Patrik Troll . . . Now, more than a quarter of a century after its first appearance, it is perhaps necessary to say that it was from Groddeck and this book that Freud borrowed the term Es (Id).

It is interesting to note that Dr. Balint was analyzed by Ferenczi, who must have established some sort of record for analyzing creative, original thinkers. Without exception, Ferenczi's analysands have shown great enthusiasm for Groddeck.

In the same issue of the *Journal* is a review, by Edward Glover, of *The Unknown Self*. Dr. Glover makes a conscientious attempt to weigh the value of Groddeckian concepts. He calls Groddeck one of the

> . . . most forceful and original of propagandists in the history of psychological medicine. He has done more than anyone else in recent times to demonstrate to a hide-bound medical faculty the universal exploitation of mechanisms of conversion hysteria, the conversion element in organic disease and the psychic gains of illness in general. To this enthusiastic interest he has coupled a passion for investigating the precipitating psychic factors in neurotic and other illness. Over and above all this, his imagination has been fired by the idea of impersonal forces manifesting themselves through various somatic and psychic activities and structures.

Groddeck came to psychoanalysis independent of Freud, contradictory as the statement seems. If we accept the obvious thesis that the type of work a man does relates closely to the kind of man he is, then the question arises: how did these two men, so different in character, arrive at so similar an understanding of the psyche?

Freud's road to psychoanalysis was through observation of the neuroses, beginning with hysteria and later extending to the obsessional and compulsive neuroses. Finally he touched on the narcissistic aspects of depression, melancholia, and, in the Schreber case, glanced briefly at the psychoses. At all times he was concerned with psychical and emotional phenomena. In fact, when in the beginning he attempted to pursue a physical course by way of neurology and the electrochemical aspects of impulses, he found it inadequate and abandoned it to work on the psychological. He did not, however, dismiss it permanently, and felt that at some later date psychology would have to be grounded in physiology.

Groddeck took a different path. He began along the lines of identification with the great healer, Schweninger. He became a physician because the profession was early set by his father's choosing him above his brothers. He used an omnipotent defense early in relation to his own father, and in fantasy saw himself a wonder-healer. Freud's dream was to be a great man—even a great philosopher; he had constantly to fight his urge to fantasy and philosophy. Groddeck began, in his work with patients, by demanding absolute obedience; no one was to question his orders or what he did. In return he promised health. (We can compare this with Freud's early work with hypnosis.) Groddeck forced his patients to regard him as an all-powerful father without realizing how he was identifying with his patients and trying to give them what, at the time, he unconsciously wished for himself.

He was literally forced into an awareness of symbolism in his patient's symptoms in the case of Fraulein G. This patient's unconscious efforts to make of Groddeck a mother figure, her desperate need combined with his intense unconscious feminine identification, were successful in forcing him to be receptive. She was treated kindly by him from the beginning and soon he saw not only the symbolic value of speech and symptoms but became aware of the phenomenon of transference. He also became aware that his patient reacted to symbols as though they were reality. In this connection it is to be recalled that Freud was forced into the reality value and potency of fantasy for neurosis by a woman patient who insisted that she had been sexually attacked by her father. On investigation this proved to be untrue, even though some of the father's behavior and feelings furthered the production of the fantasy and therefore constituted a *symbolic* sexual involvement.

Both Groddeck and Freud began their self-analyses at approximately the age of forty-two. Freud used Wilhelm Fliess as a transference figure and Groddeck used Freud in a similar manner, both mainly in letters, with occasional meetings.

The parallel between Freud's attitude toward Fliess and Groddeck's toward Freud is so striking it seems certain that Freud himself must have noted it.

Jones describes at some length how Freud made use of Fliess, who had to listen to his theories and pass judgment on them. "He (Fliess) acted in short as a censor. And a censor, besides his obvious activity in eliminating the objectionable, performs an even more important function in silently sanctioning what he has allowed to pass. This sanction is what Freud at that time needed, not the independent-minded, inflexible Freud we knew in later years, but the very different man he was in the nineties. Fliess bestowed this sanction freely . . . so the praise he gladly gave must have been highly encouraging. One example alone of its effect will suffice: 'Your praise is nectar and ambrosia to me.' " Speaking of a meeting he was to have with Fliess, Freud said he had "panted" for it, he was "in a state of continuous euphoria and working like a youth." At another time he wrote, "I am perfectly content to write only for you."

If we turn to Groddeck's letters to Freud we find the same tone, the same longing, the contentment "to have you as a listener." Likewise, as it became necessary for Freud to free himself from Fliess to go on with his work, so was it necessary for Groddeck to free himself from Freud, as he did when he began to accuse Freud of disliking his works and his concept of the It.

Freud sought and found an excuse for breaking with Fliess. Groddeck did it with accusations. For both, when the break was necessary, it came. It had to come with some temporary bitterness.

Perhaps Freud recognized what Groddeck was doing. He was not always discerning in his close relationships, but his unwavering patience with Groddeck suggests that he saw the mechanism in operation.

"There came at last a time, however, when he recognized that his depression was no longer to be lifted by the old cure, and that only courageous painful inner work would help. He decided to stand alone and fight it out . . . There is ample evidence that for ten years or so—roughly comprising the nineties—he (Freud) suffered from a very considerable psychoneurosis . . ." says Jones.

The nucleus in a symptomatic sense for Freud was his train phobia (according to Jones, leading back to fear of leaving home, mother, and the breast). Groddeck used as the symptomatic nucleus a number of "organic" diseases. The ones most prominently mentioned were thyroid enlargement and the sore throat in relation to scarlet fever with multiple determinants, including a transference wish to identify with Freud and to be loved by Freud. (Note Groddeck's associations in the analysis of the sore throat, with Freud's case of Dora.)

Yet, despite the striking similarities of the two men, there were great differences. Freud was the first-born child of a young and loving mother. Groddeck was the last-born of a rigidly narcissistic woman who used many weapons, even pregnancy, to pry admiration from her family. Freud was amply breast fed for nineteen months. Groddeck almost starved to death in his first few days.

Freud's attachment to his mother was strong, but it would appear that he handled the Oedipal situation somewhat more easily than most because of the complicated family picture. The attachment to his wife's sister and the continuing attitude of a paterfamilias suggests that a kind of acting out of the Oedipal situation was possible. The mother was always in the background and symbolically always ready to give. He was free to deal with the omnipresent fantasy of the dangerous father figure who threatens and molds his son with the castration danger.

Freud's mother was clearly delighted at her son's birth, whereas Caroline Groddeck dressed her son in girl's clothing until he was past six and sent him thus arrayed to a girls' school to be companion to his sister.

Groddeck's attachment to his mother seems a hostile identification, a kind of unity in which there was little room for an identity of his own. His early arrogance and attitudes of omnipotence, as well as later symptoms of psychic turmoil, can be seen as both an expression of and a defense against awareness of this unity. He persisted in claiming to be his mother's favorite, yet the defensive denial against a feeling of being unloved appears again and again in his formulations. The father figure is almost absent in his "philosophy."

Throughout his life Groddeck attempted to deny the fact of his father's death. He continued in his search for the vanished father, whose greatness he would support by being submissive and subservient. Even toward the end of his life, when he wanted to serve Hitler, he still sought men who might need him to bolster their strength. Freud refused to accept him in this capacity. Frieda Fromm-Reichmann suggested that, when he interpreted Freud's reaction as a rejection, and was rejected by Hitler, a psychotic episode was precipitated, but it seems that his approach to Hitler already gave evidence of the bypassing of reality.

As opposed to Freud's pervasive father figure, Groddeck's psychology emphasizes over and over unconscious identification with mother and mother figures as the power in the development of both sexes. He sees a creative wish in everyone as an unconscious wish for pregnancy. He insisted, always, on man's double-sexed nature (as did Fliess) and toward the end of his life wrote and lectured on it. The fact that later it amounted to a frantic defensive denial of his passive feminine identification cannot lessen its value as an aid to understanding the human psyche.

Groddeck made several references to the fact that he preferred to work on the relationship of his patients to the mother rather than the father. He felt, as he wrote to Freud, that this might change when his homosexuality was less defended against, and said ironically that castration anxiety cannot be bypassed by focusing on nursing and weaning. He was half serious when he related destructive drives as originating in the initial expulsion of excess parts from the fertilized ovum as a first stage in development.

Both men showed a high degree of involvement with the speculative and the philosophical. Freud spent a large part of his life defending himself against this urge, and succeeded except for occasional controlled defections. He used the need to prove and to understand as a major tool against this "pleasure principle." He also warned Groddeck repeatedly against it.

Groddeck, on the other hand, yielded easily to the urge. In *The Book of the It* he even says that he is not to be held tomorrow to what he says today. Frieda Fromm-Reichmann reports that he often said this in her presence.

The real evaluation of Georg Groddeck's contributions to psychoanalysis and psychosomatic medicine has yet to be made. Some of his theories have been proved correct and are accepted unquestioningly, as though they had always been known. Other theories have not been tested. Still others, such as the "new" attitude toward childbirth without pain, the recognition of emotional factors in hypertension, ulcers, coronary disease, and so on interminably, are making reputations for other men.

The physical life of Georg Groddeck provides many interesting bits of information which suggest the course of his development from an unwanted baby to an original and creative thinker, but there is nothing conclusive, nothing inevitable about the development. He was past forty when Frieda Fromm-Reichmann met him. She said of him, "As a psychoanalyst I should have been interested in his early life. Actually, I was not. For all I cared, he might have sprung full grown into being yesterday. He was complete, exactly right. Nobody would have wanted to change him."

Many people tried and gave up. There was a stubborn integrity there, a rock of determination. He was doomed always to seek a father, and to be rejected whenever he found one. In some ways he remained always a child, with a child's simplicity and optimism. He believed in happy endings. Perhaps that belief helped to make him the gifted healer he was. Disease was his adversary, and he fought to win.

BIBLIOGRAPHY

Alexander, Franz and Ross, Helen, *Dynamic Psychiatry*, Chicago: University of Chicago Press, 1952.

Cohn, Prof. Dr. Hermann, *Uber Schweninger's Entfettungscuren*, Wiener Medizinische Presse, Nov. 5, 1898.

Durrell, Lawrence, "Studies in Genius: VI Groddeck," *Horizon*, XVII (June, 1948), pp. 384-403.

Eliasberg, W. G., "Allgemeine Arztliche Gesellschaft für Psychotherapie," in *American Journal of Psychiatry*, Vol. 112, No. 9, March, 1956.

Erikson, Erik H., *Childhood and Society*, New York: W. W. Norton and Co., 1950.

Fenichel, Otto, *Collected Papers*, 2 vols., ed. Dr. Hanna Fenichel and Dr. David Rappaport, New York: W. W. Norton & Co., 1953.

Ferenczi, Sandor, M.D., "A Psychoanalytical Romance," in *Final Contributions to Psychoanalytic Technique*, ed. Michael Balint, M.D., trans. Erich Mosbacher and others, New York: Basic Books, Inc., 1955.

—— "Review of Die Psychische Bedingheit und Psychoanalytische Behandlung Organischer Leiden" in *Final Contributions to Psychoanalytic Technique*, ed. Michael Balint, M.D., trans. Erich Mosbacher and others, New York: Basic Books, Inc., 1955.

207

Freud, Sigmund, *The Ego and the Id*, trans. Joan Riviere, London: Hogarth Press, 1947.

—— *An Outline of Psychoanalysis*, New York; W. W. Norton & Co., 1949.

Fromm-Reichmann, Frieda, *Principles of Intensive Psychotherapy*, Chicago: University of Chicago Press, 1950.

Groddeck, E., *Vardagslivets Psykopatologi*, Stockholm: Bonniers, 1924.

Groddeck, Geo., *The Book of the It*, trans. M. E. Collins, London: Vision Press, 1950.

—— *Das Buch Vom Es*, Vienna: Internationaler Psychoanalytischer Verlag, 1923.

—— *Exploring the Unconscious*, trans. M. E. Collins, New York: Vision Press, 1950.

—— "Flight into Philosophy," in *International Journal of Psychoanalysis*, 1923, 4:373.

—— *Ein Frauenproblem*, Leipzig: C. J. Naumann, 1903.

—— "Grundsatzliches über Psychotherapie," in *Allgemeine Arztliche Zeitschrift für Psychotherapie*, 1928, 1:581-590.

—— *Hin zu Gottnatur*, Leipzig: Hirzel, 1909.

—— *Die Hochzeit des Dionysos*, Dresden: E. Pierson, 1906.

—— "Uber das Hydroxylamin und Seine Verwendung in der Therapie der Hautkrankheiten," Berlin: Buchdruckerei der "Post," Kayssler & Co., 1889.

—— "Influence of English Literature on Germany," in *Sackbut*, Vol. 14, No. 1, August, 1933.

—— *Ein Kind der Erde*, Leipzig: Hirzel, 1905.

—— "Klinische Mitteilunger aus einer zwanzigjahrigen Psychotherapeutischen Taligheit," in *Zeitschrift für Psychoanalyse*, 1928.

—— "Man's Double-Sexed Nature," in *Purpose*, Vol. 4, No. 1, Jan-March, 1932, 21-28.

—— *Nasamecu,* Leipzig: Hirzel, 1913.

—— "Psychical Treatment of Organic Disease," in *British Journal of Medical Psychology,* Vol. IX, Part 2, 1929, 9:179-186.

—— *Psychische Bedingheit und Psychoanalytische Behandlung organischer Leiden,* Leipzig: Hirzel, 1917.

—— "Die Psychoanalyse und das Es," in *Zeitschrift für Psychoanalyse,* 1925, 11:509.

—— "Uber die psychoanalytische Behandlung der Nierenstein-bildung," in *Zentralblatt für Psychotherapie,* 1928, 1:136.

—— "Psychosomatische Forschung als Erforschung das Es," in *Psyche,* 1951, 4:481-87.

—— "Rast und Ruckblick" (Rest and Review), unpublished fragment, 1929.

—— "Relation of Massage to Psychotherapy," in *British Journal of Medical Psychology,* 1931, 11:228.

—— *Der Seelensucher,* Vienna: Internationaler Psychoanalytischer Verlag, 1921.

—— "Der Symbolisurungszwan," in *Imago,* 1922, 8:67-81.

—— "Eine Symptomanalyse," in *Zeitschrift für Psychoanalyse,* 1921, 6:30-327.

—— "Traumarbeit und Arbeit des organischen Symptoms," in *Zeitschrift für Psychoanalyse,* 1926, 12:504-512.

—— *The Unknown Self,* trans. M. E. Collins, New York: Vision Press, 1929.

—— "Wege Zum Es," in *Psychoanalytischer Bewungung,* 1932-4, 161-171.

——*World of Man,* translated by M. E. Collins, New York: Vision Press, 1951.

—— "Wunscherfullungen der irdischen und gottlichen Strafen," in *Zeitschrift für Psychoanalyse,* 1920, 6:216-227.

—— "Das Zweigeschlect des Menschen," in *Psychoanalytische Bewungung,* 1931, 3:166-72.

Grotjahn, Martin, "Georg Groddeck and His Teachings about Man's Innate Need for Symbolization," in *Psychoanalytic Review*, Vol. 32, No. 1, January, 1945.

Inman, W. S., "Emotion and Eye Symptoms," in *Modern Trends in Psychosomatic Medicine*, London: Butterworth & Co., 1955.

Jones, Ernest, *The Life and Work of Sigmund Freud*, 3 vols., New York: Basic Books, Inc., 1955.

Ludwig, Emil, *Bismarck*, translated by Eden and Cedar Paul, Boston: Little, Brown & Co., 1927.

Meng, Heinrich, "Eulogy for Geo. Groddeck," in *Zeitschrift für Psychoanalyse*, 1934.

———— "Epilogue to the Eulogy for Geo. Groddeck," in *Zeitschrift für Psychoanalyse*, 1934.

Menninger, Karl A., *Man Against Himself*, New York: Harcourt, Brace and Co., 1938.

Pfister, Oskar, "Review of *Psychoanalysis Today*," in *Schweizerische Zeitschrift für Psychologie*, Vol. 9, No. 2, 1950.

Rangell, Leo, "The Nature of Conversion," *Journal of the American Psychoanalytic Association*, Vol. 7, No. 4, October, 1959.

Reik, Theodor, *Listening with the Third Ear*, New York: Farrar, Strauss & Co., 1949.

Simmel, Ernst, "Birthday Message," reprinted in *The Unknown Self*, trans. by M. E. Collins, New York: Vision Press, 1929.

Sperling, Melitta, "Psychotherapeutic Techniques in Psychosomatic Medicine," in *Specialized Techniques in Psychotherapy*, ed. Gustav Bychowski, M.D. and J. Louise Despert, M.D., New York: Basic Books, 1952.

Von der Goltz, Joachim, "The Analysis of a Dream," in *Baden-Baden*, II, 1958, 31-34.

Von Diersburg, Egenolf Roeder, unpublished paper.